Trafficking Aftermath

How to Be Happy After Trauma

Airica D. Kraehmer

Based on a True Story

Published by Storytelling Marketing CEO
Airica Kraehmer, Miami, FL.

Cover Art Designed by: Airica Kraehmer

Cover Art Photographer: Leon Johnson
(www.instagram.com/ljportraits.com)

Printed in the United States of America.

ISBN: 978-0-578-60531-9

Foreword

"**B**ut I have raised you up for this very purpose, that I might show you my power and that my name might be proclaimed in all the earth" ....

Exodus 9:16. What would you do **to** find your purpose? What would you do **when** you found your purpose?

Everyone has advice as to how to find your purpose and what to do with it when you find it. Without a doubt, God gives women strength. As with everything God gives us, we then become the stewards of that gift. We also become responsible to use it right and be accountable for how we use it. A strong-willed woman isn't afraid to meet the world head-on. She's undeterred by those who say something can't be done. Her God-given passion produces clear-eyed purpose, deep compassion and a bold spirit that has the power to change the world. But even a strong-willed woman runs into issues along her journey. Sometimes her determination and strong will lead to misunderstandings and breakdowns and the only one that can help her overcome them is **God**. Becoming a woman of strength and purpose gives glory to God and it releases you from the captivity of hopelessness and despair.

When you are going through a dark season in your life, one of the toughest but most important things you can do is trust **God**. During periods of crisis, it can be extremely difficult to understand the depths of God's love for you and the unfathomable extent of His faithfulness. If you want to become a woman of strength and purpose, you must come face to face before God and confess that you don't want to do life without Him. At this point of surrender, God will rescue you. Think of God as a perfect orchestra conductor. No matter how far off you get from the original score, God never misses a beat. He takes our mistakes, our failures and our disappointments and blends them as we go. No matter what happens, we should let go of our self-sufficiency to trust that He, our Conductor, really does know best. **To find our purpose!!**

In her first International Best-selling book **Models Stop Traffic, Airica D. Kraehmer,** a warrior of change, victim advocate and survivor-leader contributes valuable context about the landscape within which human exploitation can flourish. Although always God fearing, she became doubtful that she had God's favoritism as she bravely led us through an autobiographical tale of events leading to horrendous acts of violence and sexual exploitation that no young woman should have to endure while she is pursuing her dreams of being a model.

In **Model's Stop Traffic** Airica opened up our eyes to the potential of evil lurking in places where dreams can be made and lives can be changed. The unveiling of Human Sex Trafficking. For her main character, Daniellé, however, life was changed forever in a way no one would imagine. She tells of her horrific experiences at the hands of monsters, her sister models suddenly becoming missing, her entrapment and torchers as well as her miraculous escape from hell, as she was kept in captivity for many months. Airica leaves us with the wondering of what Daniellé does and how she gets out of this God forsaken situation as she conceals herself in a bathroom stall awaiting daylight to start her journey to safety. The cliffhanger ending compels the reader to want to hear more.

Trafficking Aftermath, Airica's newest body of work, picks up where **Models Stop Traffic** leaves off. Although Daniellé finds her purpose very clearly at the end, she starts out still in the throws of the aftermath of what happened to her as she is awaiting her opportunity to leave her coveted city, NYC, and go back to her home, where she perceives safety, love, and acceptance only to be quickly thrown back into doubt, rejection and shame for what happened to her. She is reluctant to tell anyone what really happened as she is still trying to categorize it herself. How can anyone believe what happened and know that it wasn't her own doings, how will they ever believe that she didn't deserve this or that it wasn't a result of the "big life" in NYC? Even her own family could not grasp or discuss with Daniellé what had happened, brushing it off as if it were just a simple conversation that was a normal occurrence. She felt alone, rejected and unable to communicate what had happened. Daniellé found herself without anyone to talk to or anyone that would even understand or care.

They called her a Phoenix!! In her glory Daniellé was vibrant, touting her flaming red hair, mighty in her stature never to give up or be hindered. Now, she felt as if fallen, she referenced herself as the black Phoenix which was a term she claimed, fallen into the ashes unable to shower off all of the ashes that had appeared during her captivity. What she was unaware of was that the Phoenix was unlike any other and that it stood out because of its feathers, symbolically referencing renewal, resurrection, of life reborn anew and transformation into power and strength. Daniellé needed to step into her ownership of being the Phoenix once again.

In her darkest hours Daniellé was about to end it all, she felt that she was unlovable, unworthy and incapable of leading a life of significance anymore. She could no longer uphold the covenant of all she valued. She had a face to face conversation with fear and felt she had lost. There was nothing else to do. There was no one that understood, that could help her, so therefore she was alone!! She wanted to end it all. But somehow was stopped.

Her journey home was not as she had hoped, it was hallowed because her purpose had not yet been revealed. Her **personal affliction** was going to be her secret, hers alone!! Writing began to be her passion, her outlet for what had happened. She wrote about her experiences, disappointment in her savior for not protecting her and how she had felt abandoned all over again. He had lied to her; He had let all of these bad things happen to her; she screamed at him!!! How could she move on? Rejection from those she loved and respected as well as herself, was intolerable. The fallen Phoenix was now seen in its entirety. She was done!!

Yet she heard Him, she obeyed!!! She heard "Not yet"!! "Tell it"!!

Why? She found her answer!! **She was the Why!!!**

How does one recover? How does one continue on? Daniellé had a purpose. This was her story. This was her WHY!!!! Daniellé Surrendered!!! She needed to become the **Model who stopped traffic**!!!

Airica, the international best seller, the advocate for those who have lost their voice, the one who will change the narrative for those that are exploited, who now has found her **WHY**, is an amazing young lady who has the courage of the Phoenix, has once again learned her purpose through her

Savior and has the ability to change the world and has begun her journey through both local advocacy as well as international organizations targeting the modeling industry to stop trafficking from ever occurring again.

It is my privilege to know her and to be considered one of her mentors as I have become one of her mentee. You have my heart and soul, **I will love you forever!!**

Wendy L. Elliott, MBA/HCM, M.A. CCC-SP

Co-Founder The Elite Foundation

Combating Human Exploitation in all its ugly forms!!

Reviews from *Models Stop Traffic*

Couldn't put it down...

"A must read- for every woman, parent, young adult going off to college... I found it intriguing to understand the psychology behind such a prevalent epidemic. I am so incredibly proud of the author for being strong enough to not only escape and survive, but to be vulnerable enough to share her journey. The world needs more women like you."- A.R.

Very informative!!!

The story was heartbreaking, but it had to be told. The primary character in the book was "groomed", misled, then ultimately drugged and raped. I don't want to give too much of the story away, you need to read for yourself! This happens more often than people think and many people don't realize this is human trafficking! - *Michigan Girl*

... model myself years ago I too went thru some horrible experiences and it did put me in some unimaginable ...

Being a model myself years ago I too went thru some horrible experiences and it did put me in some unimaginable circumstances. To this day I wish I had the "knowing" and support. What a great book and a remarkable woman, thanks for writing part of my story. - *Tracey S.*

Eyes Wide Open!

IF you know ANYONE who wants to become a model, or an actor/actress, PLEASE "gift" this book to them OR their parents because it will open their eyes to what goes on in so many of these industries...GLOBALLY. I deeply appreciate Author Airica Kraehmer's mission to spread this vital message, to inform, and empower those who are considering these as career paths. - *Jackie M.*

Dedication

T hese words, from my soul to this book, are for the ones whom are seeking happiness after tragedy. I give my strength, love and knowledge for you, this way, you too can overcome the difficulties of loss, despair and PTSD. Let this text fuel your hope in pursuit of liberty, justice, and happiness.

Prologue

S upermodel Coco Rocha is known for walking Paris Fashion Week, Marc Jacob campaigns, and Vogue. Few know her for Rocha for Senhoa, a complete fashion collection movement dedicated to helping Cambodian victims of human trafficking.

English actress, Julia Ormond, is known for her films *Legends of Fall* and *Sabrina*. Most do not know about her foundation, Alliance to Stop Slavery and End Trafficking (ASSET).

All the worldwide laughs from *That '70's Show*'s actor Ashton Kutcher are more recognizable than his nonprofit, *Thorn*, saving children around the world from sex slavery.

Yet, these movements are not nearly as discussed as the glamour of the runway or television screen. The topic of human trafficking not nearly as picture-perfect as Rocha's eyes, Ormond's elegance, and Ashton's well...everything.

Rescue and prevention of domestic and global human trafficking affects every type of demographic from the top shelves of celebrities and millionaires to every impoverished corner of the globe.

Human trafficking touches the lives of suburban school children, top New York City fashion models, foster children, and millions of other vulnerable individuals. Traffickers trick the vulnerable with promises of a better life or through kidnapping unexpecting victims. In some cases, before even a day into their new reality, victims experience violations of human rights through the destruction and abuse of their bodies and souls.

With no promise of rescue, a victim is never guaranteed to become a survivor.

With a lack of knowledge and vital resources around 17,500 individuals are trafficked into the United States every year. This number representing only the documented cases through law enforcement and hotlines, and not the thousands of individuals who go unheard annually.

Traffickers exploiting these victims are leading to a global $32 billion dollar crime. A complete industry flourishing on the abuses of humanity.

****

Daniellé Winters was now a human trafficking survivor as she sat on the floor of a New York City hotel. She felt like she had stayed here for an eternity. If her bones had decayed, and flesh decomposed, in her mind, her outside would match how she felt inside.

Daniellé had survived violation after violation. She had fought, ran, and lived, but to what end would this matter?

She no longer felt alive.

The time in between primal instinct to *fight at whatever cost* and *being able to breathe again* is blurred. People do not discuss what it takes to survive, and most do not realize just how far they are willing to go to make this happen.

Daniellé had no clue how to explain what happened to her family or if she should tell them. In their eyes, Daniellé was light-hearted, outgoing, not the dark monster who would kill to be able to obtain freedom. Sharing this monster with others meant sharing with your parents that at one more violation, rape or beating, Daniellé would have killed someone or herself to prevent the ongoing torture.

It is impossible to explain that to the ones who loved her. This meant, the time between primal instinct and breathing again means keeping silent. It means wearing a mask and keeping a secret for a chance at normality again. It meant keeping the spotless family reputation and not discussing the tragedy. It meant not destroying her parent's hearts with the truth.

For Daniellé Winters it meant living like *it* never happened.

Daniellé had survived human trafficking, but she would forever be alone. She would forever be silently tormented.

Perhaps, it was a cosmetic joke that she had been trained as a model. She had been trained to wear a mask and walk tall and boldly despite inner emotions. No one would know the mask from reality. Her training was going to help bridge her from victim to survivor.

But that was not going to be enough for her trafficking aftermath.

Table of Contents

Section One: Shutter

It sounds like Daniellé was the type of girl, who would conquer a storm to save her life,

But being marked for trade would mean to bear arms of weapons.

It sounds like Daniellé was the type of woman,

Who would drape herself in dreams, joy and graceful love,

But being marked as a target would mean a change of heart.

It sounds like Daniellé was the type of person,

Who would see how good can be afflicted by so much pain,

Being marked as a victim would mean to never again be the same.

It sounds like Daniellé was the type of human being,

Who would shutter herself away from the world who stole her light,

Being marked as trafficking aftermath would mean to live with the remains.

I Was Here

There is a fine line between the fate one chooses and the destiny one cannot escape. Perhaps, there is free will, and everything that happens in a lifetime is the result of a series of a person's past decisions. If so, perhaps reincarnation exists, and the faults of past lives accumulate to cause consequences and tragedies. This would mean everything that had happened to Daniellé was a result of something she had previously done.

They say only the good die young. This concept would lead to the idea that previous decisions of one's past reveal their future. Thus, life is dark-rooted in nature, and an *eye for an eye* quickly becomes an eye for an *arm and a leg*.

Then there is the idea of inescapable destiny. An idea in which free will does not exist and the narrative of our lives was decided before a person's first breath of air. Romantically speaking, soul mates destined to meet one another in a coffee shop could fit this theory. The thought of a newborn baby being designed and created perfectly for its parents sounds beautiful. But this idea of destiny is heartbreaking as well. For it would mean everything that happened to Daniellé was going to happen despite any choice she ever made. Her pain and torment was not preventable.

If a person had made the type of horrid decisions leading to their torture, rape, or death in a previous unremembered life, then the circle of life may be fair.

But is it right?

Should someone be punished for actions they committed in another life, even if they do not recall them?

Or is someone is innocent and destiny forces them down a path of pain and horrors, is this right?

Daniellé was not sure if she should believe in either theory, but then again she was not sure if she believed in anything anymore.

****

The hotel sinks faucet's water rushed down in white bowls as a hotel guest cleansed her hands. From under the restroom's stall, Daniellé saw a pair of knockoff designer heels at the washing station. She could tell the studs of the black shoes varied in the shapes of pyramids along with an off-centered logo - dead giveaways.

In the past, Daniellé would care, but as she saw the knockoff shoes walk away, she felt indifferent.

It seemed pointless to care about such frivolous things now.

Daniellé gave herself a pep-talk as she rose from the floor. *Okay. Just get through the day.* She thought.

After leaving the restroom, Daniellé attempted another call from the hotel's guest phones, dialing Gabriel's number.

"Hello?" Daniellé asked.

"Hey! Daniellé. Been a minute, are you at Catolyn's place?" Gabriel immediately asked.

"Not yet," Daniellé responded.

"You still have the info?" Gabriel questioned.

"Yes, just haven't made it that way yet. Trying." Daniellé was beginning to flounder in her words.

"Good. She is a nice lady and a good friend of mine. You should call your dad. Is your phone broken or something? I tried texting." Gabriel was beginning to ask questions Daniellé did not want to answer.

"Yeah...it's dead." She answered with an ironic thought. *Like my soul and dignity.*

"Yeah, you are terrible at charging electronics, and for that matter, answering your phone in general. Well, call me when you get there, alright? But I gotta get back to work." Gabriel's tone was lightly teasing.

"Yeah, will do. Thank you." She answered as Gabriel hung up the phone.

Daniellé did not even have the chance to ask about the advice she really wanted, but perhaps that was best.

Walking down the streets had Daniellé extremely paranoid. After several blocks, she managed to find enough change for a subway pass, but the subway would only help her get within six blocks of Catoloyn's home.

As she exited the subway station, she found herself in the personality of lower Brooklyn. Entirely different than Manhattan, free-spirited people roamed the streets in hipster attire instead of business suits. Some of them even danced and sang on the streets as if a concert was happening just for them, while others painted beautiful murals on the sides of buildings. Daniellé was bewildered like Alice was in Wonderland.

If not for her current circumstances, she would have enjoyed this place a lot more. Wishing she could belong, she walked to Catolyn's address.

The music faded in the distance as townhouses with Victorian iron bar gates entered Daniellé's vision. She was close now, and a few blocks later she found the stranger's home and Daniellé's safe house.

As she approached the gate her throat clogged. Daniellé knew almost nothing about who lived in this home. Gabriel assured her it was a safe place and Catolyn was a good person, but that did not mean much to her. After all, she no longer believed people really knew anyone.

Gabriel did give a few details about Catolyn, though. He expressed she was a phenomenal Broadway singer with an extremely positive attitude. This is what Daniellé used to power her decision to push open the iron gate and trudge to the singer's front door.

After a few minutes staring at the door. She knocked, and the door swung open almost immediately.

A high-pitched voice greeted Daniellé, "Oh, aren't you just lovely - a true doll face!

Daniellé mentally began to panic as Catolyn reached to hug her. Frozen she tried not to scream despite the agony of pain to her arms and waist. She was not entirely sure what was wrong with her, but even the slightest touch felt like a million knife stabs at once. Seeing a doctor was on her need-to-do list, but priorities told her to find a safe place first and deal with the medical aftermath later.

"I'm Catolyn. A pleasure to meet you! I heard New York City was giving you some trouble. Come in." Catolyn greeted inviting Daniellé inside her home.

I can still run away. Daniellé thought. *But where?*

Realizing Catolyn was her best option, Daniellé followed her inside.

"Well, no worries! We have the happiest house in all of lower Brooklyn!" Catolyn assured.

Daniellé was now puzzled. *We? What had Gabriel told this lady? Why does this place smell like cookies and raisins?*

"Are you the quiet type? You look like you could be? I do not mind if you are or...are not? I just can kind of tell what type of people are what type of people, ya know? And you look like the popular introverted type. But your hair gives a different impression -flaming red is bold! An expression of deep passion and intensity! So, which is it?" Catolyn directed Daniellé to a living room navy love seat as she walked to the open-room kitchen island

Daniellé had lost track of Catolyn's thought process three sentences ago.

Catolyn reached for a kettle to pour herbal tea into a couple of *Beauty and The Beast* themed mugs. Catolyn's hair resembled the famous princess Belle's hair -long with curls. She looked mid-thirties but held the cheerful aura of a child. Her curves were the type Daniellé did not possess, and her height could be no taller than 5'5". Daniellé thought Catolyn was alluring with a unique beauty as the woman stood in the kitchen.

Daniellé did not answer Catolyn's questions quickly enough as the singer changed the topic to her tea set. "I am a huge Disney fan. I have my own personal little chipped cup too. I call him Chunk, not Chip, though, for originality sake." Catolyn burst out a hearty laugh.

Daniellé liked people who could laugh at their own jokes. "That's funny." Daniellé approved.

"She speaks!" Catolyn exclaimed. "So which is it?"

Confused Daniellé asked, "Which is what?"

"A broken extrovert or an introverted extrovert? My vote is a popular introvert. A model with flaming red hair seems ironic," She mocked, "Let me be silent in this photo while captivating all eyes on me." Catolyn explained in another confusing manner.

Daniellé had never thought about it that way.

"Umm...the first one? Maybe? Not sure," Daniellé answered.

"Well, then we best fix that chip right up! See, I only have only room for one Chunk." Catolyn said as she lifted up her cup, "The world needs your joy. Did Gabe tell you I sing? I met Gabe like fifteen years ago when I was getting started. Now, I am in that play *Wicked*. The one with all the posters on the taxis. You like broadway?"

"Yes, I do. Hamilton and Chicago are my favorites," Daniellé smirked.

"That is good. I will put some music on then! Have you eaten? I am thinking of cooking pasta. I have not had any company in a minute with lots of shows lately. You see that room over there?" Catolyn pointed, "That is David's room.

He is a director, a really good one. He has been working on a Netflix series. You know who Bill Nye is?"

"The science guy?" Daniellé questioned not sure where this was leading.

"Yeah. Bill Nye the science guy. He is working on revamping a show for Bill. I'm sure it will be a hit." Catolyn spoke highly of her roommate. "David won an Emmy. I am sure you will notice it tonight."

"Like a *real* Emmy award?" Daniellé was already impressed.

"Yep! I already asked him if you could stay in his room since he is gone. He is cool with it. You would like him, a swell guy." She expressed.

"Oh, I am fine on the couch. I do not want to get in the way." Daniellé expressed politely.

"You would be in the way if you were on the couch!" Catolyn added.

"Thank you. Yeah, probably. Can I ask you something Catolyn?" Daniellé was hesitant.

"Call me Cat." Catolyn nodded yes.

"Cat, like the CATS musical?" Daniellé attempted a joke but gulped, "Do you know why I am here?"

"Not much. Gabe told me his friend was struggling and needed a safe place to crash for a night or two. He helped me out once, so I just said yes. You look harmless, but you should get that arm checked out. Did you run into something?" Catolyn expressed motherly concern. "May I take a look?"

"Sure..." Daniellé exposed the deep wound on her arm.

"Well, one thing is for sure. You are in luck!" Catolyn covered the wound back over.

"I am?" Daniellé was not convinced.

"Yeah. I know first aid. You should go clean it." Catolyn smiled pointing to the restroom.

Daniellé silently agreed.

"Goodie! I don't not have much food here, but I am going out anyways. Be careful to not let the water burn that area. It is cut pretty deep." Catolyn suggested as she stood to gather her purse and jacket.

"I do not really have other clothes with me." Daniellé pointed out, slightly embarrassed.

"No problem. I already set out some towns, a shirt and gym shorts. Oh, and David's bed sheets are clean just in case you were wondering. I will be back in a jiffy." Catolyn opened the door to leave.

Her voice is even lyrical. Daniellé thought after Catolyn closed the door.

Daniellé sat on the love seat in stillness as she looked around the room. The herbal tea's scent of orange spice was now masking the cookie and raisin smell. Even without Catolyn physically here, the rustic brick and wood home was still lively. The walls were lined with hundreds of books and even an old-fashioned record player was in the corner. She had never seen one of those in person. The open kitchen-living room had glass cabinets revealing ceramic Disney-themed dish ware of all the princesses. There was even a *Wizard of Oz* decorative plate.

Slowly in pain, she stood to walk into David's room. The sunlight peeked through a single window. The room was tiny and definitely belonged to a filmmaker. Instead of books or music, movie posters and media equipment lined the walls and shelves. A top-notch Mac computer was bigger than the twin-sized bed in front of her.

Daniellé imagined after a hard day's work, David would open the door and land face first into the mattress. His shoes may have even stayed on if he was tired enough.

Daniellé thought it may be nice to leave him a thank you note, but for now, she needed to decide what to do about contacting the police or a doctor.

Was it worth going to the police? She thought.

Surely, they would not what she should do.

Then she saw it in the center of the wall on an eye-level shelf. In all its glory, a shining Emmy award stared at Daniellé, and she stared back at it, amazed.

David must be the real deal.

Daniellé could only imagine the fulfillment with earning one of those prized statues.

Thoughts flooded Daniellé's mind. This all couldn't be real. Maybe she hadn't escaped and was unconscious again.

But she wasn't. This was all real, happening right in front of her eyes.

These people were living their dreams. They were thriving and represented what Daniellé wish she had - New York City successful creative careers.

Her dreams were broken, and from the looks of her body. She was quite literally fragmented.

She could still feel the lashes of the men who had beaten her. She could still feel the forced entry of the men that coveted her. Her arm continued to bleed off and on; her feet torn to pieces from mysterious surfaces. Her legs were decorated with purple and rouge bruises.

Daniellé was no more than inches from the Emmy award on the shelf, but she essentially thousands of miles away, and perhaps even thousands of lifetimes away, from an Emmy award.

She studied its appearance in longing as her hand slowly reached out to its smooth surface.

"Phoenix. They called me a phoenix." Daniellé said as she picked up the award carefully.

She held it with both hands as it reflected her swollen face in its shine.

"Does that mean I will rise from here? Like what? Air?" Daniellé scoffed as anger built in her.

She placed it gently back down to its shelf home. Daniellé turned to the bed. A fluffy sky-blue towel greeted her. She picked it up with its matching washcloth and David's spare gym clothes.

Daniellé as the fallen phoenix, needed to decide if she should shower off some of those ashes.

At Variance

The morning light filled the room for five hours before the melatonin lost its effect on Daniellé. David's high-tech alarm clock buzzed, and Daniellé wondered what exactly was in the orange spiced tea Catolyn provided at last night's meal. She stood up slowly from the ground as she reached for her right side of her ribs.

****

She had attempted to sleep on the bed but each time she shut her eyes she was back in that house with men over her body. The floor did not help, but she lay awake there staring at the ceiling until daylight.

"Something terrible must have happened to you." Catolyn commented starting a conversation.

Daniellé could not get a grip on herself long enough to answer. So, instead, she just returned her hand to her lap and looked toward the bookshelves beyond Catolyn. She did not want to seem rude, but she had no clue how or if she can answer with an explanation.

"I will live." Daniellé quietly stated.

"That you will!" Catolyn latched onto the small hope Daniellé expressed and ran with it. "And you will be better for it. And you will grow from it! You will do something just as great because of such a hard fall."

"You are definitely the hopeful type, aren't you?" Daniellé said sarcastically.

"You have to be. It is the only way to survive in this city." Catolyn stood in a laughing with a sitting superman power pose.

"This city may just kill me." Daniellé responded dryly.

"Only if you let it!" Catolyn smiled not knowing the reason behind Daniellé's words.

The remaining time eating dinner was entertained with small talk.

Catolyn placed the dishes on the kitchen counter and walked toward her room. Daniellé provided her a thankful look for not pressuring the prior topic, and she sauntered toward her borrowed refugee of David's room.

"Thank you, Catolyn. Truly." Daniellé said before opening his door.

"You are most welcome. Goodnight." Catolyn smiled widely.

✳✳✳✳

Daniellé left the memory as she completed a small stretch cycle. Daniellé opened the wooden door to expose the kitchen and living area to the window's morning light. A note on the kitchen island from Catolyn expressed that she had a last-minute fill-in show for a cast mate, and she would be home close to 3:00 p.m. With the note was seven dollars and twenty-four cents, and directions to the deli down the street. A BLT special included a sandwich, drink and fries.

Daniellé smiled at the precise change and kind gesture. Thoughtfully, Catolyn had even washed her clothes last night. Daniellé thought about if she should put them back on her still unwashed body. She saw A phone next to her note.

Daniellé returned the note to the corner as she picked up the phone and charger. She brushed her hair while she waited for power. Afterward, she made her way to the couch. Most would think that the first number she would call would be her father's, but Daniellé wanted to come to him with answers, not worry him. She loved her parents, far beyond what they probably thought. Daniellé always wanted to stand on her own feet, and she did not want to ever appear weak or be a burden to her parents.

Her parents were young. They had Daniellé in their teenage years. She knew they were still growing up and finding themselves. If they were still figuring out their own lives, how would they have time to sort through their daughter's needs. They could not.

So, instead Daniellé called Angelia, and she acted like nothing was the matter.

"Hey, glad you answered!" Daniellé greeted.

"Oh. Hey, girl! Didn't recognize the number. What's up?" Angelia answered excited. "Any exciting New York City news?" Angelia was just as fascinated with the fashion industry as Daniellé.

In a way, Angelia was living through Daniellé.

"You know me. My life is always full of excitement." Daniellé was not lying, but her voice cracked.

"That is cool! Boring here as always. I hate work so much." Angelia complained.

"Can you do a favor for me?" Daniellé asked. "Yeah, what's up?" Angelia questioned back.

"Can you look up Landon Kents number on Facebook?" Daniellé faked a laugh in hopes Angelia would not catch on to the weird request.

"Sure. One of the pilot friends of yours right? I think we are friends on Facebook. I will look him up. You guys talking or something? What about Daryl? Is Landon like a rebound? Eager Angelia wanted to the latest gossip in Daniellé's love life.

Daniellé's heart sunk. Her love life was once chaotic, but now it was dramatically and permanently ruined. She had already deemed herself as unlovable. Before she at least could stumble about trying to uncover the key to how to make a relationship work.

Daryl needed distance when she left. She could say Angelia's assumption of a Daryl rebound was a little insulting, but it was better than the truth. The truth for Daniellé was moving forward she could never be purely loved.

She would have a stain of pitch blackness in a fragmented heart. She could not share the depths of her experiences, even if she wrote a book to the world in explanation. No man or woman would be able to reach her in this pain, and for this tragic alignment of events she would never be saved by a prince. She would never be fully accepted with her wench mark. She was polluted, valueless, and inoperable. Daniellé paused before answering.

"A girl can't help but rebound, right?" Daniellé threw out a light-hearted question to prevent a lie.

"I got you! Yeah, I will text it, but I should go to work now. I just answered randomly thinking it could have been my bank calling me back." Angelia laughed.

"Well, I am glad you did. I miss you." Daniellé said.

"Me too. Call me soon. This place is not the same without you." Angelia was distracted by someone in the background and hung up the phone.

"I love you." Daniellé said, but her friend was already gone.

Daniellé switched out David's clothes for her cleaned attire. As Landon Kent's number popped on the screen of the phone, Daniellé wondered what she would tell him. As she slipped on her shoes to walk to the deli, she dialed.

"This is Landon." Landon answered confidently.

"This must be your business voice." Daniellé laughed.

"Huh? Oh, Daniellé? I know that sarcasm followed by a laugh anywhere. What's up?" Landon asked.

"Umm...funny man,but hey, Landon. Is there any way you are doing any flights home from New York City soon? I hate to ask. I was kind of...mugged." Daniellé again felt safe in the fact that she had not lied.

"Damn. Are you okay? I do not have any flights, but I check to see if any of my buddies do or if I can switch. Let me pull it up." Landon began searching as he conversed.

"I'm kind of roughed up, but I am alive. I just want to go home for a little while to you know..fix everything." Daniellé said as nonchalantly as she could fake.

"Completely understand. I can use one of my passes to get you to Charlotte then fly you home myself tonight if you want?" Landon advised.

"You would be my hero." Daniellé thanked him.

Landon loved the idea of his ego struck, and found it fitting to be a hero.

You know I will take care of you. Let me send you everything and call my buddy." Landon assured.

"Thank you so much." Daniellé commented before they hung up.

Daniellé suddenly felt a little more hopeful. She greeted the deli master with her exact change and with the comment about the BLT special. The deli master had a roaring laugh as he said she must be a friend of the woman who comes in here every other day.

Daniellé sat quietly in the back corner as she devoured the BLT and fries. A few of the deli patrons stared at her. An old businessman looked out of place for this section of town as he finished his newspaper. He set it down on the table when finished and placed a coffee cup to his lips. Daniellé stood up to approach him in inquisitiveness.

"Umm...sir?" Daniellé asked for a moment of his time.

"Yes?" The man looked startled at her appearance.

"Is there any way I could read the cover story of the paper? If you are finished?" Daniellé smiled.

"Oh, sure. Take the whole thing. I am done with it. Nothing ever really changes in the world." He spoke in his business tone.

Daniellé smirked in approval, but she did not find his joke funny. He was doing her a favor, after all.

"Thank you." She said as she picked it up from the table.

Daniellé was not really interested in the cover story of the newspaper. In fact, she only had one interest, the calendar date.

When she saw it, her eyes wanted to protrude from their sockets. It was almost a week and a half later than she thought, and she wondered why no one thought to ask why they had not heard from her. Did they not talk to her that much, or did time in New York City really move faster than the rest of the world?

Daniellé read the newspaper as she waited for Landon's returned message. When it arrived thirty minutes later, she perked up at the news. The flight would be at 7:00 p.m. and depart from JFK international airport. She was not familiar with JFK, but it appeared this would soon change.

She messaged Landon how much of a hero he was for helping her out like this. He replied to let her know he would have a friend waiting to help her at the airport.

Then the residual thought reentered her mind. *I should go to the police.*

In the past, Daniellé had never had much experience with law enforcement, but she knew she needed to talk with them.

But was it safe? Were the people of the house involved in what happened? Was it all a coincidence of aligned tragic events -or was it all tied together.

That was just it though. It was bigger than those four people who betrayed her, but it was also so much bigger than her alone.

How many people truly get away from what those people were doing?

How many people live?

No doubt, they were looking for her. No doubt, she should be afraid and cautious. But did she not have a responsibility here? If she decided to keep her mouth shut, it was aiding them in taking countless more girls, right?

She did not want to do it.

She wanted to board the plane, and she wanted to pretend this chapter of her life was never written. She wanted to hide for the remainder of her life. She never wanted to be touched again by a man. She did not want to think of how much of an idiot she was for letting this happen. She just wanted to move on with her life.

But she couldn't. She could not just leave.

What she wanted did not matter. Hell, the more she thought about it, no one got what they wanted. Everyone lost. Some lost their money. Some lost their dignity. Some lost their hopes and dreams.

She lost...everything.

So, it was decided.

The first step in moving forward in life was sacrifice. Daniellé was going to have to find it in herself to be strong enough to do this. She was going to have to go face-to-face with the fear that taunted her. It was all great pep-talk in a Brooklyn deli, but the reality was far less inspiring. But it was decided, Daniellé would go to the police before stepping foot on that plane.

When 12:00 p.m. ticked around, Daniellé met Catolyn at the front door. If she had arrived with anything, this would have been the classic suitcase scene like in the movies. Catolyn knew immediately it was time for her new friend to leave. A sad expression captured Catolyn's face and transferred to Daniellé.

"So, soon? Are you going to be okay?" Catolyn asked as she set down her purse. "You sure I cannot make us some more tea or something? I am actually craving some green tea."

"I am sorry. My plane departure is at 7:00 p.m." Daniellé answered. "But hey look, it means everything to me that you and David let me stay here. It is just, I need to get home, and I think I should go to the police about what happened. I think I have to…"

"That is the most you have spoken since you walked in! I knew you were just a broken extrovert. If you need to go to the police, there is a station nearby. I can go with you?" Catolyn attempted to be chirpy. "Well, at least take this with you. Gabriel told me it is to help you get home. He also mentioned that he called your dad. Don't worry about the money. It came from your dad, anyways." Catolyn handed Daniellé a bag with a subway pass and some cash.

Daniellé smiled, "Thank you."

A sad Catolyn opened the door for her as she left. Daniellé had learned something in these fleeting moments.

The developing of a friendship cannot be labeled by the amount of time spent with a person or how long they are in someone's life. If life was as simple as chronological time the doctor who delivered someone should be their best friend and number one on speed dial. Instead friendships should be labeled based on the experiences shared and the intensity of those times. The best friendships can form in the middle of chaos, and the most unsettling times of one's life.

This was the type of friendship created here between Catolyn and Daniellé. If ever blessed with a new opportunity to see her again, Daniellé hoped it would be in the type of circumstances in which they both thrived.

Thy Neighbor Rejection

Finding police stations should really be a lot easier.

Daniellé walked up to a police car with an officer eating lunch. She tried to politely knock on the window for his attention. A frustrated man set down his Pepsi and packed lunch. He gave Daniellé a disapproving look for her interruption. She did not mean to ruin his break, but she was confused on how to find the police station.

The police officer was the most logical person to ask, right?

The man looked Daniellé up and down for her level endangerment before exiting his car.

"I am sorry to bother you on your break." Daniellé mentioned first. "But can you tell me the direction of the station?"

The hungry officer did not speak to Daniellé. He only pointed to the left before getting back into the car. Daniellé was put off by the idea of going to the police by the guy's gesture. She even thought it could be a horrible, weak excuse to not go, but she shrugged it off.

After walking a few blocks more, Daniellé saw police cars line the sides of the streets. It was like the yellow-brick road of the ultimate neighborhood watch. Daniellé wondered if this street had a lowest crime rate in the city.

She reached the cracked concrete steps of an old faded brick building. When she opened the door, she saw a line of people waiting to file police reports. She stepped in line not entirely sure what to do or what she would say. After she signed a clipboard, the police station attendant told her to take a number a seat. Twenty minutes passed as she watched numbers be called to meet the attendant at the door. It was hardly private as people provided loud complaints about their neighbors.

When Daniellé's name was called she walked nervously toward the door. Through a six inch crack of the door, a mid-fifties blonde woman peeked her head out with a clipboard. It reminded Daniellé of the gatekeeper from *The Wizard of Oz*.

"So, why are here?" The blonde asked nonchalantly looking at her clipboard.

"To report...umm..an assault?" Daniellé whispered.

She felt uneasy talking so publicly through a cracked door. She may have been over thinking it, but she felt like everyone behind her was eavesdropping.

The woman lowered her clipboard and opened the door wider.

"How about you come in here?" The blonde woman's tone had changed from nonchalant to a concerned mother's voice.

Daniellé agreed and followed the woman's hand gesture to enter the back rooms of the police station. Everything she saw seemed to be stuck in the 1930s. The woman led Daniellé to a bare-walled, cream-colored room with only three chairs and small wooden table.

"Take a seat here. Would you like a glass of water?" The woman asked.

Daniellé's mouth was dry, but she shook her head no. The woman left to search for a detective. Daniellé sat waiting for about thirty minutes until a tall much older gentleman with a mid-western accent entered. The blonde woman trailed behind him with more papers and her clipboard.

"I'm Detective Carl," He greeted with a smile,"I believe you want to report an assault?"

This man was supposed to help her, but Daniellé felt more nervous now than the suspension of waiting. She did not understand how a man was supposed to help her when men were the ones who caused her pain in the first place.

He and the lady with the clipboard seemed to be her only options though. Daniellé began with telling them about how she was working as a model. Then she explained all of the strange happenings occurring in the apartment she shared with the other models. She began stuttering when she recalled the drugs, nightclub assault and the other house. She explained all of the rapes she could remember, but she knew she was still missing some of the memories.

With every statement, Daniellé saw the men of the house attacking her. As if they were here with her, she could hear their threats to kill her and her family.

The detective and his colleague absorbed each word in silence. The blonde woman tried to look away when tears escaped her eyes. Daniellé did not mind her tears though, as silent tears ran down hers as well.

Daniellé held her composure until the last few sentences until she collapsed into tears on the wooden table feeling violated all over again. She felt like she just had lived each experience all over again.

No one spoke for several minutes.

A box of tissues was handed to Daniellé by the woman.

"So, none of what happened. Happened here in this district Manhattan or different house in Brooklyn?" Detective Carl asked.

Daniellé nodded yes.

"But Daniellé, you should know I can only submit this report to those districts. I can't guarantee they will take it. It is out of *this* jurisdiction." His words had an undertone of powerlessness as he spoke.

He could see the despair in Daniellé's green eyes. She was fighting a fall out, and there was absolutely nothing he could do but send an email or phone call? Daniellé's head bowed down with her hands meeting the temporal sides. An intense headache developed.

She was left in the room with two blank sheets of paper for her statement. She stared at the sheets feeling hopeless. How was she to describe coherently and concisely what happened on these pages. She had no idea how to start again. She could write thousands of words and hundreds of pages, but she had only two.

Help me. She thought.

When she finally ran out of room from even the sides of the paper, she stood, but instantly, lost her balance. The detective had started another session with someone else, and the lady with the clipboard had returned to her daily activities. They were quickly back to business as usual.

When she realized they were not coming back, Daniellé left the papers with her statement and walked out of the station.

She had failed.

No one cared what had happened to her or the others. Her fate was in the hands of an email that may or may not be sent. The voices of the model apartment girls echoed like a nonstop recording in Daniellé's mind as she entered a taxi headed to the airport. Everything flashed by quickly as the car made its way to JFK. The taxi man tried to converse with her asking about her flight plans being leisure or business. Daniellé faked a smile, and then she stared back out the window. The driver did not attempt conversation again.

A couple hours later, Daniellé found herself sitting in row "F" of a plane headed to Charlotte, North Carolina. Toddlers cried around her, and silently she joined them. They were scared to go up in the air at night. Daniellé could empathize. Now, she too, was scared of sitting still in the dark in someone else's control.

Carry Me Home

"Danielle, I have a friend from the airport security waiting for your arrival. We are lucky I happen to be flying back to Georgia tonight." Captain Landon Kents encouraged Daniellé with a phone call.

"Yes. Lucky." Daniellé's words were barren.

She felt agony, pain, anything but luck.

Daniellé had not explained the details to Landon. Landon asked no questions, but went into rescue mode. Fortunate for her, Landon was a man of action rather than words type. Anytime he could spring into rescue mode he went full speed ahead. Even if was a little bit dramatic for the situation. Ironically, for the reality of this situation, it was appropriate. Daniellé remained closed off from the details.

"Thank you, Landon. This really means a lot. I got that flight to Charlotte, but I will not arrive until almost 10:00 p.m." Daniellé explained.

"I know. That is fine. I thought you may be a little pressured with time. So, you have been transferred to the 10:45 p.m. flight, and I will have my friend or myself meet you at the gate. It will be a smooth transition. I promise." Landon's tone of voice was heroic.

"Thank you. I will see you then." Daniellé quietly said.

Daniellé hung up the phone to switch it to airport mode. She desired some peaceful silence.

The flight to Charlotte was loud with six babies continuously crying. By the time it ended, everyone looked like they could use a drink from the closest airport bar. Since the flight attendants had run out of water before reaching her row, Daniellé was out of luck.

Storms delayed exiting the plane for over twenty minutes. During this time all six babies on board engaged in a cry competition. Nonetheless, when Daniellé finally walked out the gate and into the airport, she felt a little safer.

The escort must have received a photo from Landon of Daniellé or she was the only one that matched her fire truck engine hair. Daniellé asked the gatekeeper to verify his position and working status before taking any steps closer to him. If she had learned anything it was to not trust anyone on what they appear as or what they say they do for a living.

He introduced himself as Officer Parks to Daniellé. "Let us put you a little at ease and take you to Landon. He is a good friend of mine."

Daniellé followed the man to the gate number Landon provided earlier. She made him walk in front of her though. She could not stand the idea of someone following behind her. When Landon appeared in eyesight, her heart rejoiced. This was the first known, trustworthy face she had seen in months. The first person she knew as a genuine friend.

God bless. It's nice to see him. She thought.

Landon and Daniellé stood hugging in the middle of the high-traffic North Carolina airport. She understood Landon arms around her were intended to comfort her, but her pulse quickened and airway started constricting. The loving touch of an old friend, who ironically was the captain of her departing home flight, to anyone else would be soothing. Daniellé did not feel at peace. She felt terrified of her friend and confused as to why.

A silent tear from Daniellé's cheek reached his shoulder. A flashback from their first fight flickered through her mind.

In an underground parking lot, Landon was in a full-on debate with Daniellé about southern women. Despite her protest of not being classified as southern, she had let him win to prevent hellfire. Daniellé recalled him sweating furiously from the heat of the summer.

****

Standing here, now, like an ice princess, she doubted having the pleasure of being classified as a southern woman ever again. Southern women possessed charm, virtue, and kindness. Qualities she doubted would exist in her again.

Her mind was tormented her in this innocent friend's embrace. In prevention of having a tear-soaked uniform, Landon pulled away keeping his hands-on Daniellé's shoulders. He attempted to mask his astonished facial expression as he scanned her bruised body, silently.

Stammering Landon assured, "You will be okay, now. I will get you home."

Daniellé gave a tight-lipped smile for him. "Okay." She said looking into his eyes.

Both startled from the moment, they looked at the gate clerk adjusting the gate's microphone.

"Hello, my name is Rhonda, and we will begin the boarding process for flight 276 to ATL airport in fifteen minutes. Please, have your flight information ready and know your group number. Thank you." The gate attendant announced.

Now holding Daniellé's hands, Landon genuinely began smiling.

"That is my cue if we want to get home tonight," Landon said jokingly.

Landon turned to his security friend, "Thanks bud. Let Cynthia or me know if you need anything."

Daniellé saw through the tall glass windows as Landon walked onboard the plane. The night stars were playing absentee, but the runway lights lit up the runway in red, white and gold.

The connection between models and airplanes formed in Daniellé's mind. An outright illegal fantasy of strutting down the airport runway in Marc Jacobs attire captivated Daniellé.

Without time for much pondering, her fantasy ended as her legs bolted toward the closest trash can. Hovered over a trash bin, in front the airport's crowd she vomited profusely. Bystanders covered their mouths in disgust as they walked down the aisle. After three minutes of embarrassment she felt her eyes flooding. Shaking her head in defeat she realized even the thought of her dreams, passion, career, and basically her whole world caused physical sickness.

Is this how I am to live now? Daniellé thought.

Officer Parks placed his hand on Daniellé's back shoulder, but she struck it away violently. Shocked he waited for her next move.

"I'm sorry. I just can't handle touch right now. I didn't mean to hurt you." Daniellé apologized heavily.

His guard lowered as he led Daniellé to Rhonda. The attendant appeared annoyed until she saw the officer's badge. Now, for her it was a matter of determining if Daniellé was a criminal. Rhonda gave her an inquisitive, yet judge-mental look. Little did Rhonda know Daniellé had seen far worse actions in comparison to the short woman's unkind gesture.

Without a proper greeting, she asked for Daniellé's flight information and personal documents. The officer handed her a small booklet with a gold stamp on it. Rhonda opened it, and her whole demeanor changed. Daniellé had learned through hours in several lines, it was possible to fly without identification. She wondered if the booklet was her proof and ticket.

Now welcoming, the attendant said, "Welcome aboard, Miss Winters."

Officer Parks nodded as he wished her safe travels. Daniellé entered through a tunnel that led outdoors. It felt like twenty degrees as she walked up the stairs to the plane. Landon gave her a flirtatious wink from the plane's cockpit. If he had seen Daniellé a few minutes ago, vomiting out her guts, he considered otherwise. Daniellé was directed to the back of the plane, past most commercial seats.

The seatbelt looked more like the type found on helicopters rather than the traditional commercial flights.

"Looks comfortable enough." She muttered.

She began to wonder if this was for her safety or others. Alone, she felt like a prisoner again. The lines between free and incarceration blurred in her mind like oils from paintings.

"Hi, I am Cynthia. You must be Landon's friend!" A peppy voiced greeted Daniellé looked up at a young woman dressed in a flight attendant uniform. Cynthia wore an ascot which matched her copper hair. Her face showed a lifetime of joy with laugh lines around her mouth, but her eyes showed days with no sleep. Daniellé was not in any place to judge though with a recovering black eye, countless injuries, and hair unbrushed since Catolyn's house. Her peppy voice displayed a love for her job as she continued without an answer from the seated redhead.

"Just so you know, anything is available to you. Coffee. food. And I might be able to swing getting you a shot." Cynthia giggled.

Cynthia paused as if she was trying to remember something important.

With eyes wide open in discovery Cynthia suddenly commented, "Oh, anything but WIFI. I have a Nicolas Sparks novel you could read? It is a short flight though, so be weary, you might get hooked! Then you might have yourself heading to Books-a-Million in the morning!"

"Thanks. That is okay though. I will probably just try to sleep a little. If I could have a water though, that would be great." Daniellé's mouth was still pungent as she spoke, but she spared the flight attendant the reasons.

"One water, pillow and blanket coming up. It might take me a moment as the other passengers are beginning to board. I oversee the exit rows, so got to go get some of those verbal commitments." Cynthia said happily.

Over the intercom Landon was greeting everyone with the expected arrival time of 1:53 a.m.

Daniellé smirked.

Her head was pounding with a dehydration headache. The seat did not lean back, so she tried to position herself as horizontally as possible. She drifted away quickly to sleep.

Mile High Nightmares

Daniellé slept motionless in the back of the plane as it departed from Charlotte. Her red hair covered the light from penetrating her eyes. Daniellé's dreams were anything, but delightful.

****

"Daniellé!" The plane was midair as someone from a distance screamed her name. Cynthia was nowhere to be found.

Daniellé unfastened her plane's seat belt buckle to search for the scream's source. Standing up, she could see passengers sleeping, reading books or watching movies. No one seemed to be alerted by the screams but her.

Now identifiable, Rana's scream was clear, "Help! Help me!"

Down the aisle from her, Daniellé saw a black figure dragging her former roommate and friend toward the front of the plane.

"I'm coming!" Daniellé's voice cracked as she yelled.

As she ran forward, passengers turned toward her with disapproving and mischievous looks at her.

"What are you all doing? We have to help her! Some stop that guy!" Daniellé commanded her new audience.

The faces around her transformed into deceptive grins, laughing at her desperation. Ignoring them, Daniellé ran toward Rana, but now instead of Rana was her former roommate Savannah. Confused but determined, Daniellé felt tugs at her blouse and legs.

When she looked backward she saw the dark grins of the plane's passengers ripping and scratching at her body. Trying to trap her in their demonic grips they clearly were on the side of the black figure Daniellé was trying to stop. Savannah's voice was falling faint as Daniellé fought off they overpowered her.

"Rana! Savannah! Fight him!" Daniellé was in agony as she spoke.

"Falling to the plane aisle's ground, her head hit the armrest of 22D's seat. As she looked up she could see a flight attendant with Richmond's appearance approaching her. He grew larger with traits resembling the demonic appearance of the passengers. His laugh was piercing as he stood in front of the injured woman.

He leaned downward inches from Daniellé's face to taunt her, "You will never escape this. You will always be mine. My bitch, my slut. You belong to me."

He straightened his back as he struck his fist across Daniellé's face.

With another blow, she shrieked. "God, help me!"

****

Daniellé gasped for air as she launched forward in her seat. Lightly, Cynthia touched Daniellé's shoulder.

"Are you alright dear? Was it a nightmare?" Cynthia was concerned.

Daniellé gasped for air as she reached to touch her bleeding head from the nightmare, except there was no blood. Her fingertips were bare. Richmond was not here. She was okay, and it was all a nightmare.

With panicky eyes, Cynthia asked again if her passenger was okay.

Daniellé nodded, and Cynthia handed her a Dasani water bottle, blanket and pillow.

"You know, I don't not know you or your story, but if you need someone to talk to. I can get someone to watch my section." Cynthia offered.

Daniellé could see her appearance terrified the flight attendant. After all, Cynthia's imagination could go rampant with thoughts of who the girl was, why she was her, or what she did to be in this awkward situation.

Perhaps, this is how everyone would see Daniellé moving forward -if she could move forward in life. Daniellé's thoughts of a future beyond this moment seemed unlikely. Part of her wished she did not have the choice to move forward -that part of her wanted to die instead.

Great. Is this how it is going to be? People scared to look or be around me? The question kept repeating in her head.

According to her nightmare, she was always going to be what she was in this moment - a slut, valueless and ruined beyond repair.

She was not even sure if she could go back to how life was before she left for New York City, let alone move forward. For now on, she was the property of someone else, a transactional item, not a human being with a soul.

"It's okay. Sorry, I just, it was just a nightmare, you know? Thank you for the water." Daniellé was embarrassed, but grateful.

The words brought relief to the flight attendant.

"Okay. Nightmares can be awful things." She smiled empathically. "We will land in about thirty minutes if you did not hear on the intercom earlier? I would have brought all this sooner, but you passed out before even lift off. Must have been really tired."

Daniellé guzzled down the water. Kathleen once told her taking phentermine for weight loss gave her dry mouth, but was worth it. Kathleen stayed small, and that is a requirement for the modeling industry. Daniellé was missing her friend as she had a similar hydration craving.

Daniellé's face was hollow as she reflected. She could have left when Rana left the house. She could have never spent another moment under the tyrant's rule. She could have left with just a bad taste in her mouth instead of the feeling of an invisible parasite living in her body.

She did not know her roommate's fates - if they had been like hers or if she was alone.

Daniellé's mind flipped back to Kathleen. She already missed her soft-hearted presence. Yes, they had their fair amount of disagreements. Everyone was always fighting in the model apartment. It was part of how the agency controlled them, but Daniellé would have never wanted this for any of the other models.

Daniellé was desperate for answers; she even thought of praying. She was not sure if there was a point to pray anymore, though.

Are they dead? Worse? There are far worse things than death. Daniellé's thoughts were miserable.

The plane's landing was smooth. Over the intercom, Landon thanked everyone for flying with American, and wished them safe travels. Daniellé wondered if he always shared this degree of hospitality. With his beach blonde hair and blue eyes, he was charming naturally. Yet, while most of his passengers were glad to hear of their arrival, Daniellé felt shame, guilt and defeat.

She was never meant to return here. Her dreams were ruined.

"So much for getting out of small-town USA." Daniellé muttered. "I guess this is what they mean when they say if you can make it in New York...but I didn't make it in New York. It nearly killed me. Some cruel joke."

Cynthia walked up smiling. "Landon asked me to tell you to meet him at the gate. It will take him a few minutes to pack up and everything," Cynthia said with glee from her shift being over, "So, are you and Landon together? I didn't think he was committing type. No offense if you are together."

With a puzzled face, Daniellé was not sure if she should be insulted. To her, Landon was not the settling down type either, but it was not really either of their business.

"Just friends, that's all." Daniellé replied.

Cynthia looked relieved, "Well, I hope you have a great night!"

Daniellé unfastened her seatbelt and laid the blanket over the seat. She was among the last people to leave the plane. In front of her was a Portuguese grandfather and his grandson. The boy was no older than three years old. He was fussy and giving his grandfather a difficult time. When he saw Daniellé the boys eyes widened in fear. Finally, someone was acting accordingly to her appearance.

Daniellé kneeled down to the boy's eye level to show she was not a threat. "Oi!"

She waved her hand in a folding style to greet the boy. Now, he clung to his grandfather for protection. At least, she knew she had a promising career scaring child into behaving for their guardians.

At this time of night, the airport resembled a ghost town. Most of the restaurants and shops were closed, and it looked more like a scene from the old movie, *Left Behind*. Daniellé sat down between a Cinnabon and Quiznos.

Looking at her phone, she turned off airplane mode. Messages flashed across the screen before she could even read them along with the chime of a voice-mail.

"Wow." Daniellé's voice echoed through the empty terminal.

Most of the messages asked if she was okay. Gabriel had provided her father with the phone number, and Angelina had given Daryl the number as well. She guessed Angelina was team Daryl.

Daniellé did not want to go home tonight. She couldn't stand the idea of either of her parents seeing her this way. What would they think of their broken and bruised up daughter?

One messaged read of Daryl asking if he needed to pick her up from the airport.

Daniellé did not like the idea of asking Daryl for help either. She was supposed to be an independent woman, but the fact of the matter was that she had no money, no car and no dignity left. She needed help, and she needed Daryl.

Daniellé sent one message stating three little letters that drilled in her defeat.

Yes.

Her fingers pulled back her hair from her face as she leaned over with her head between her knees. With each exhale, she listened to her breath rise and fall. It was a technique a former yoga instructor taught her to relax.

It was not working.

Lifting the phone to her ear, she dialed its voicemail. She expected the message to be from her mother or father, but it was from a detective.

"Hello. This message is for Daniellé Winters. My name is Detective Carroll Lewis. I am calling on behalf of a report you filed with Detective Carl. Please, give me a call when you can. Thank you."

The message ended with Detective Lewis repeating his phone number twice.

The call would have to wait until morning. First, she needed to figure out what to tell her parents.

"You on the phone?" Landon walked toward his friend smiling.

He removed his flight uniform hat and loosened his tie. His ivory muscle shirt outlined his sculpted abs, as he rolled a small suitcase behind him. He stopped in front of the red head.

"It's nothing." Daniellé tucked her phone back into her pocket.

The crew began to exit the tunnel behind him with Cynthia among two young brunette flight attendants. They gossiped inaudibly, but they were clearly looking at them.

"So, do you need a ride somewhere? You know you could always stay at my place too." Landon offered as he reached for her hand.

Daniellé's sweaty palm gave her the freedom to breakfree easily. She clasped her hand to her waist for security.

Landon may have thought Daniellé was just playing hard to get and he continued his offer, "I know you have experienced something horrible, but we have been friends for a long time. You are safe with me."

She could not be mad at Landon for trying. There was no way he could know what her last few months of hell were like. She knew he was innocent of all of this, and he was supposed to be her midnight hero. But something was building fury within her as he seemed to be asking for a midnight booty call. She wagered which would be the least likely to attempt anything with her tonight - Landon or Daryl. Her bet was on Daryl.

"I am really thankful. You have helped me so much, but I have someone coming to pick me up." Daniellé spoke softly.

Landon was disappointed but still whispered in her ear, "Another time then."

Daniellé wanted to vomit. Not because she didn't find Landon attractive. She knew she did, but because his tone of voice reminded her of *the carasser*.

Daniellé turned to catch up with his coworkers. Perhaps, he was even looking for Cynthia. Daniellé walked along following them until she saw the signs for baggage claims and arrival pickups. She waited on the steel benches for Daryl's arrival.

Making use of the spare time, Daniellé called her father. Secretly hoping he would not answer, she let out a sigh when it went to voicemail.

"Hey Dad. The plane landed. I am safe, but going to stay with Daryl tonight. I am just not ready to come home yet. Please, don't be mad. I love you." Daniellé fought back tears as she pleaded for him not to be angry.

She did not want to try so hard to speak with her parents. She wanted to be the successful, obedient, loving daughter they always wanted. The bitter truth was it had almost always been difficult for her to talk with her parents.

Her mother had run off marrying another man when she was a young teenager. Daniellé and her younger brother had not liked the man in the slightest, but her mother did not seem to care how they felt. Daniellé's father was the biggest introvert she knew. He once told her he would run off to a private Caribbean island by himself if he could. Maybe he had never noticed the pain those words caused, but she had felt rejected by her parents throughout her teenage years.

She had bottled up all the pain, just as she did several times before, and shielded her parents from the horrific truth.

Daniellé was not sure why she kept staring at the baggage claim. It had nothing to give her, but as the minutes ticked on, she thought she best try to look presentable when Daryl arrived. As she walked toward the restrooms a small Korean girl walked out bumping into her.

"Sorry." She apologized.

"It's totally okay." Daniellé answered.

A full-length mirror captured her reflection as she entered the restroom. It seemed every time she saw her reflection, she felt sick at the sight of herself.

Daniellé's fading red hair gave a new definition for the word disaster, and her swollen eyes and bruised face reminded her of an old history channel show about child labor laws.

"Put on a pretty face and don't let them see you weak." She recited to herself, trying to believe her own words.

Pumping cheap, hand soap into her palms, Daniellé began the double cleansing method for her face's oily skin. Her left arm would not raise high, so instead she bent heavily over the sink's surface.

Surely, cheap soap is better than no soap, right? She thought as she carefully avoided pressing too strongly into her wounds and bruises.

The sink's white bowl filled with tainted greenish brown water as she cleansed. Once she was finished Daniellé patted her skin dry with a few tan recycled paper towels.

She knew eventually the bruises would fade and the wounds would heal. Soon no one would look at her like she was a monster, and she would appear as if nothing ever happened to her. She just didn't know if the inside would ever heal.

Daryl

Danielle was startled by a loud vibrational ring from such a small phone.

"Hello?" Daniellé answered Daryl's call.

"Hey! I'm out front. Where are you?" Daryl's voice was groggy.

"Oh, okay. I'm outside arrival pickups. I will go out now." She replied.

As she set down the phone, the memory of Darly dropping her off at the airport surfaced. The day before her departure was filled with so much hope. They had spent it together, and now she was swiftly lost in the memory.

****

"You know what?" Daryl sweetly spoke as he tousled Daniellé's hair.

The pair had made a habit out of making out in his car even though they lived together. She knew not to take Daryl to serious. He was all fun and games, and she was positive he loved his car more than he cared about her.

"I know a lot of things, but I have a feeling you have more to add to the collection?" Daniellé replied flirtatiously

The only person debatably more quick-witted than her was Daryl. His clever imagination could go anywhere and it showed in all his writings. His latest novel was still a secret to most, but Daniellé was pretty sure she was the muse for his female character, Bonnie.

The two had this invisible but known, *Don't Ask, Don't Tell* policy. It prevented this fragile friends-with-benefits arrangement from falling apart.

"You are like a butterfly. The type always heading for the horizon." He postulated.

Daniellé sheepishly smiled as she looked away. When he stated romantic nonsense, her whole idea of him not valuing her feel apart.

Her lips moved centimeters from his left ear as she teased him, "And what butterfly am I exactly?"

His back straightened as he sorted out the question in his head, "Hmm...Lycaenidae."

Daniellé laughed as she flung the car door open. When emotions would become too heavy, Daniellé immediately wanted to run away.

There is a buddhist saying explaining how one will be calm when they meet their soulmate. They won't feel nervous or anxious, but instead it will feel like being with your best friend. Daniellé tried to live by the saying. Hoping it was true as it guided her decisions.

Her heart was never calm with Daryl, but a constant fluttering of butterflies and sweaty palms. According to the buddist, it would never last between them.

Autumn leaves still covered their yard from the previous spring. Under an oak tree, her body was tackled in loving embrace to the ground by Daryl.

Leaves flew everywhere.

"I thought you were going to rake these!" She laughed.

Daryl pivoted onto his elbow to hover over Daniellé as he remarked, "You know I can always catch you. So, why run?"

With a handful of leaves, Daniellé surprised attacked him, starting an autumn leave war in spring.

****

Daniellé returned to present day. The memory was nothing but history. Sure, she would still be a runner, but the touch of a man and the thought of being chased terrified her.

The memory was no longer pleasant through today's looking glass. She could no longer be with Daryl. If she was a butterfly, now she was permanently changed. If she was once alluring or seductive, now she was disgusted by the thought of someone seeing her in such a manner.

Daryl leaned against his car outside. Daniellé saw him through the glass window walls of the airport. It felt like a foreshadowing truth. Daryl and Daniellé would always be separated by invisible barriers.

They would always be able to see each other, but not reconnect. She didn't want to share what happened in New York with him. She did not want to explain what those men had done to her, and that meant she could not be with Daryl either. She could not be with anyone in that way again. Therefore, she would break his heart to protect herself from any more damage.

Like a scene from an Audrey Hepburn movie, Daniellé began running through the doorway to Daryl. He encompassed her in his arms. She ignored the pain desperate to feel safe. His heavy laugh and embracing arms held her without words for what could have been forever if they allowed it. His chest was warm, and his heartbeat strong. Daniellé did not feel the panic attacks arising in these moments. Her guard was lowering, and she felt safe.

In this moment she was okay.

In this moment, she could breathe and no one could hurt her.

No one could beat her...

No one could cut her insides...

No one could rape her...

This was the moment Daniellé longed for and even if it was short-lived, it was still hers. It was a moment she could hold onto, maybe even provide hope for her future.

It was not enough though as it faded too quickly.

It was too different. Pulling back from Daryl, his deep brown eyes were more shallow than last spring.

Daniellé accepted it. Daryl wanted to fight it. Yet, neither had a choice in the manner.

Daryl opened the passenger seat door for their long car ride home. The living room's lights glowed from the house as the car was parked in the driveway. The leaves had disintegrated and everything appeared surreal to her. The steps welcome mat was titled in the same position as she left it months ago. The door creaked as it always did. The living room still smelled of cherry blossom and baked goods - the cross scent between Daniellé and Daryl.

Time had stood still here.

"I will go start a shower for you and pull out some products you left behind," Daryl suggested.

He walked through the kitchen to the back bedroom. Daniellé's feet felt cemented at the foyer. She stood still as she thought about what it would be like to be back here again.

She could stay in hiding. Let everyone think she never returned here.

After all, she was never meant to return.

Everyone would think of her as the girl who escaped the small town. That would be the story gossiping through town square and hair salons.

"I left some clothes next to the sink along with a glass of water and ibuprofen. It looks like you might have a headache. That is the only time you are quiet. There is a towel and some travel products in the restroom." Daryl's voice sounded exhausted.

"Thank you." Daniellé moved toward the restroom, "Daryl, can you get me a blanket for the couch?" Her voice was equally tired.

"How about we figure that out after you shower? No offense, but you smell awful." Daryl laughed.

Daniellé closed the restroom door behind her. The bathroom filled with steam and the hazy mirror comforted an unseen Daniellé. She picked up the medicine and water glass. Her throat was aggravated by the shallowing sensation.

As the adrenaline rush tampered off. She decided to be bold. Using the towel, she wiped the remaining steam from the mirror away.

She slowly stripped off her jean shorts from her legs. At mid-thigh, they fell to the ground. She stepped slowly out of the individual leg holes. Looking down, the jeans were stained from lingering blood. Bruising had developed near her cervix and cuts were infected. Daniellé stared at the mirror instead of directly at her body. The reflection was the only thing separating her from herself.

At one point in time, Daniellé's body was beautiful. Years of healthy eating, daily workouts, and spa pampering. Years of lotion application, scar prevention, teeth whitening and pedicures. Beauty routines and self-care was religious for her career. Now, she was ruined.

Furiously, Danille struck out her anger at her drinking glass. It crashed to the bathroom shattering into pieces. She could hear Daryl's rushing footsteps over the shower's water.

"Daniellé! Are you okay?" His voice was urgent. "Let me in?"

Daniellé's gemini personality split. A small part of her wanted to let him in to rescue her from this monster overtaking her body. This part of her believed she could be saved, fixed or anything more than a battered girl on his bathroom floor.

The other part of her wanted to shield him from the monster inside his home. She was a danger to him. In just a matter of a minutes being here, she managed to break something already. The darkest parts of herself were in control, not her. If she let Daryl in, she could hurt him too.

Daryl didn't stop, "Let me help you. I am not mad, okay. I just want to know you are okay?"

Daniellé's hand turned the knob slowly from the restroom's floor. A rush of steam flooded the door's crack opening. Covering the lower part of herself with the towel, Daniellé allowed Daryl to enter the room.

His astonished eyes scrolled down her mutilated body. She was less than one hundred pounds of ramshackle. Daryl tried to hide his horror, but her appearance matched his facial expressions. He kneeled to the floor with Daniellé seeing the glass surrounding her.

"I broke it. I am trying to clean up the pieces before I shower," Daniellé's voice sounded unintentionally cruel.

Daryl's stronger hands reached for her to drop the pieces into his palm.

"I thought you had fallen. I will get the broom." Daryl said sweetly as he stood.

He lifted her directly from her kneeling position to sitting on the sink's countertop. She looked away as she winced in pain. In the past he had always tried to be gentle with her, but now he could not be vigilant enough.

"Stay here, please. I don't want you cutting her feet." He requested as he left for the kitchen.

Cutting her feet did not seem to matter as much as it should to her, but she obliged his request. She watched him sweep the floor carefully.

"If you wanted me to clean, you could have just said so." Daryl made light of the situation, but the false joy did not even convince his eyes.

"I'm sorry. I know you are tired. I'm being a hassle." She apologized looking at her hands.

"The only hassle you are being is refusing to take a shower. Looks like I am going to have to make sure this happens." Daryl said.

His broad shoulders and toned biceps lifted her again from the counter to the shower. Her mind screamed as the towel fell, but her voice was silent. Daryl did not look down, but she was internally panicking.

The water was lukewarm, but it's refreshing serenity encompassed her. Daryl applied body wash to a cloth. "Here."

Closing the curtain, he left her.

Danielle remained on the shower floor, knees to chest until the water ran cold. Water with hair-dye, blood, dirt and sweat rushed down the drain. She didn't move, but just watched the water run until it was clear of her remnants. The water camouflaged her tears. She thought after concealing her tears for so long, they would now rush out of her like an unleashed dam. Instead, her tears fell individually.

After her shower, she dressed and met Daryl in the living room. His look was undeniably distraught.

Is my despair contagious? She questioned.

The marks on her body were exhibited more clearly now. Her pale skin and hair amplified their boldness. She looked like half a person standing in front of him with oversized clothing.

"Thank you for creating me a bed. You work the early shift tomorrow?" She asked.

"Yes. I will leave here around 4:00 a.m. Your car is still in the garage by the way. There are things in the fridge if you are hungry. Knowing you, it will be more like lunchtime by the time you wake up." Daryl yawned in between his words, "But this is not for you. You can take my bed."

Daniellé's gag reflex activated at the thought of a bed. Darly noticed, confused.

"Or...you could sleep out here?" He quickly added. "Can we both stay out here?" Daniellé asked.

Daryl let out a smiling sigh, "Sure. Not practical and a waste of my awesome bed, but sure. "Let me find a couple more pillows. I will set up the other couch."

Daryl left the light on as he watched Daniellé fall asleep.

Interspecial Couples

Morning light filled the living room as a bird continuously squawked outside. Daniellé had forgotten where she was momentarily as she jerked upwards. The living room clock read 9:36 a.m. Daryl had been gone for hours. He most likely was reviewing the previous night's monstrosity. A note laid on the coffee table in front of her with Daryl's handwriting.

I had forgotten how you slept like a rock. Muffins in the fridge, clothes in the dryer, cash in the envelope, mail on the counter, Daniellé on the couch. He wrote.

As Daniellé folded and put away the bedding, she almost felt like this could be home again. The clothing from last night was in the dryer except for her shorts. Those were placed in a Kroger bag on a door handle.

As she consumed banana nut muffins, Daniellé researched walk-in clinics on Daryl's computer. A clinic was in her section of town about ten minutes away by driving.

The envelope had $25.00 in it. Enough money to cover getting to the clinic and to her father's house. Daniellé smiled at Daryl's generosity. He was stringent with money, so this was a highly meaningful move on his part.

She wanted to remember him forever just as she thought of him in this moment. The man who would go to great lengths to see her smile. The man who would protect her and watch over her as she cried to sleep. It gave her a small hope for humanity in men.

Daniellé opened both garage doors to see her dusty blue car waiting for her return. She started the engine for it to run for a few minutes before going to the clinic. As it ran, she looked through the car to see if anything could be useful to her. All she managed to find was a tweezers, an issue of Vogue from last year, and a half empty perfume bottle.

Daniellé remembered Daryl mentioning mail. It was most likely just junk, but it was worth sorting through as she waited.

Junk. Credit Card Offer. Bank Statement. Junk. Letter. She read.

She walked back into the garage holding the letter. The note was unusual and had no return address. Flipping it over, Daniellé ripped the seal.

Wherever you go. I will follow. Whoever you love, I will know. You belong to me. It cryptically read.

How was this possible? Daniellé thought as her heart pounded faster and airway closed.

She leaned against the car door for support, but she clasped to the ground. She heard the squawking bird as her eyes closed.

She woke up to a young neighbor leaning over her.

"Hey. Are you okay, lady?" The boy poked at Daniellé as she regained consciousness.

He looked to be around six years old, and he rode a green scooter. Daniellé leaned up.

"Yeah, I am alright." Daniellé lied.

"Okay. You know that's a weird place to nap. I am not supposed to be here. Something my mom said about interspecial couples. Whatever that means." He said is a confused boyish tone.

Daniellé genuinely laughed.

"Interspecial couples are the ones that love each other so much that they love one another despite their differences." She explained.

"Well, that means my parents are interspecial. They have a ton of differences." He insisted.

"I am sure they do." She replied standing.

"Well, I gotta go." The little boy picked up his scooter as he waved goodbye.

Daniellé felt dizzy as she sat in her car. After a few minutes, she pulled out of the driveway.

A silent prayer escaped her lips, "Please, let that house find love again, for Daryl's sake."

Section Two: Raw

The sharpness in you and the raven blood in me, is the clarity in me and reason for you.

The pain running through me, and the bleeding of freedom from you, is more soothing than the pain they gave to me,

So I thank you.

And the fall from the bridge is shorter than the fall to my knees, and my bloody razors understand God isn't listening.

The drugs go down almost as easily as the pounds from the scale and hair shedding from me,

This place isn't my home and somewhere between here and there I lost something once told to me was my soul

Won't this world leave me or I return to it?

So, greet me with the only feeling left as I am ready for the fall to bleed into ground which I came,

There is no help left to give me so it's better to leave the world by your merciful blade.

Health Clinic

I've never been to a county walk-in clinic." Danielle stated to the lady at the front desk.

"Fill out these papers." The lady behind the desk was the classic vision of an overworked employee.

"Okay." Daniellé said as she walked away from the desk.

The room was filled with pregnant couples, a few overweight men, and a woman in her forties. Daniellé sat between the woman and a biker-looking man.

Daniellé did not want to complete paperwork. She did not know how to explain why she was here by checking boxes. Daniellé wrote a false name on the sheets, classic Jane Doe. She wanted complete discretion.

Tobacco? *No.*

Children? *No.*

Exercise? *Yes.*

History of Depression or Mental Illness? She left it blank.

The next question angered her.

Have you had sex with more than one person within the last 12 months?

Sex...

Could a health clinic combine repeated unconnected sexual assaults in the same category as merely changing boyfriends or one night stands?

Daniellé noticed the lady looking down at her paperwork. Daniellé had been circling the question repeatedly. The stranger's judgmental look forced Daniellé to look straight forward.

She was not scared of the woman's judgment. After all, why did this woman feel the right to read her answers or judge her was beyond Daniellé's comprehension.

Daniellé turned the clipboard over, and walked back up to the clerk's counter.

Her voice was angry, "I do not want to complete these papers. The questions are insulting. I just need to talk to a doctor, please."

The woman disapproved at first until she glanced over the forms.

"We will get nurse Kelly to see you as soon as she can, but she is at lunch currently. I will call you when she is here." The clerk calmed her.

Daniellé waited and waited, awaiting to hear her name called.

"Here." Daniellé said.

Raising her voice hurt her throat, abs and chest. The nurse directed her to the room to take her vitals. She insisted on giving Daniellé a speech about a healthy body weight for her height. Daniellé just nodded. She had heard this speech a thousand times. Afterwards, the woman led Daniellé to a waiting area.

A lady with olive-skin and platinum hair greeted Danielle, "Hello, my name is Kelly. Can I get you to follow me?"

The whole building was off-white with no decorations. It was a vast contrast from private clinics with fancy paintings, children centers and fake plants.

They entered room six.

Kelly asked Danielle to take a seat. Danielle started fidgeting with the paper sheet on the patient table as Kelly looked over the few forms she completed.

As she laid her clipboard down her hands tucked neatly into her lap.

After her pause, Kelly continued, "There is not much here to go off of. Would you like to talk about why you are here today? Anything you say to me is confidential."

Nurse Kelly reached over for the tissue box.

"I don't need those," Danielle said with her eyes following the box. "I did not like the questions, that's why I did not fill out the paperwork. They were insulting."

At first, Daniellé could not get words to form. It was as if she was Ariel from *The Little Mermaid*. But then, it rushed over her.

It wasn't words at first, but tears.

This time is was exactly like an unleashed dam.

Wailing.

Bellowing.

Gasping for breath.

It was the hardest, most painful cry of her life. Daniellé could not even grasp the tissue box Kelly was trying to hand her again.

Daniellé just laid back on the table in excruciating physical and emotional agony. The crying caused her to clasp her waist and the gasping breath burned her throat. The emotional crying caused more pain-induced crying, and it went on like a never-ending cycle.

When she was exhausted and eyes burned too much to cry further, she felt numb.

Danille moved into an upright position facing a patient Kelly. Daniellé choked on the first attempts of words, but Kelly still patiently waited.

Looking at her body to find somewhere to start, "My chest and wrist hurt," Daniellé stuttered, "I am bleeding a lot too. I have been for days. It's not my cycle."

Calmly, Dr. Kelly stood from her stool.

"Let's start with your wrist." She said.

With no x-rays, Kelly hypothesized Daniellé had a possible rib and wrist fracture.

Kelly asked Daniellé to lay down on the table. She listened to various areas along her chest and back as Daniellé breathed.

"After a long period of listening, Kelly spoke, "I hear a murmur in your chest, but it could be nothing. I think it would be best if we took a full exam with a doctor and a few blood tests."

"It remains confidential?" Daniellé asked. "Entirely."

Kelly confirmed.

Daniellé followed her down the hallway to a darker lit room. As they entered the room she stopped to close the door behind them.

She turned back in concern and seriousness, "I will only ask this once, and you do not have to answer me. Do you want to tell me what happened? If you are okay with it, we should do a full STD screening and pregnancy test."

With a large inhale, Daniellé stared at Kelly's eyes.

Kelly knew she had been raped, but she was trying to be kind about it. She was trying to be gentle with her patient.

"Yes." The words pierced her own ears.

"We need to do a full exam, okay?" Kelly commented.

This time all Daniellé could do was nod yes. Kelly asked Daniellé to remove her clothes from the waist down and handed her a standard patient covering sheet as she left the room.

"Take your time. I will be back in a few minutes with some help."

It was only a couple minutes but waiting for Kelly to return felt like waiting for paint to dry.

"Are you ready for us to come in?" She kindly asked.

"Yes." Daniellé anxiously replied.

An Asian woman followed behind Kelly, and the examination began. Kelly informed Daniellé she was taking a few swabs for various tests. Daniellé was asked to provide a blood and urine sample, treated and bandaged.

The Asian woman suggested Daniellé go to a hospital or specialized care soon. Daniellé agreed with a nod, but she was not sure if she could do that. She didn't want her parents to know about what happened, and her insurance would definitely tell on her.

"One final thing," Kelly's voice was motherly again, "I can understand if you don't want to talk to us, but please talk to someone."

She handed Daniellé a plastic bag with psychologist and women's care information along with toothpaste, abuse help brochures and anything else Kelly could manage to cover up the real purpose of the bag.

"Thank you." Daniellé commented.

The ladies left her to dress again, and once ready, Daniellé left the room.

"You do not owe anything. All set." The clinic cashier replied.

"I do not understand? Not even for the tests?" Daniellé asked.

"It is taken care of." He repeated.

Puzzled Daniellé turned away from the counter. Down the hallway, the Asian lady stood against a white wall. It was as if she was staring into Daniellé's soul.

"Okay, thank you." Daniellé said to the gentleman.

Her hand reached out for the exit doorway to the lobby, but her head turned back. The asian woman was gone.

Fashion Affliction

S ome foolishly, optimistic person once said, "Success is the ultimate revenge."

That somehow being successful in life will fix all the wrongs that occured. Removing a person's cruelty is not as easy as waking up one day in a comfy bed. Daniellé wondered how people lived like that.

How could any of this ever get better? Would she ever trust a casting call, management team or modeling agency? She had been betrayed before by lying agents, producers, friends and exes, but nothing cut as deep as a scam agency.

They had made her a living corpse.

How could success as revenge fill such a gaping void?

Daniellé could not even find the strength to try.

The rain poured hard on Daniellé's car as she drove through her hometown. Everything looked the same, even though she felt so different. It was the same people, roads and routine. In this moment, it was not much annoying as heart wrenching for her to see. It was like an animal been pinned back into its cage.

Maybe this cage was where she belonged. Maybe this was the universe's way of sorting out the mistake of letting her escape the town in the first place.

After the clinic, Daniellé just wanted to feel safe. Her headaches began resulting in her vision going white, thus making it impossible to drive safely. She pulled over the car next to Ray bridge. This bridge had been under construction since before she left. Daniellé could not remember when they first started building it, but she knew it had been years.

An unfinished bridge meant privacy as she walked its narrow path. Here was her ultimate runway test as each step needed to be precise in order not to fall. Removing her shoes she walked barefoot along its edge, she recalled a time where she was terrified of heights, especially bridges over water, but now she kept stepping along without thought.

Daniellé stepped out to the center of the bridge facing the water. The rain lightened, but she was already soaked.

I wouldn't have to feel anything. She thought.

It was hard to tell what time of day it was from the clouds, but in the distance she could see cars filled with people either heading to lunch, happy-hour or home.

I wouldn't have to feel anything. She repeated the thought.

The murky waters current beneath her was angry and overflowing.

Would it kill me or just hurt? She pondered at her suicidal thoughts.

Daniellé was typically not the suicidal type -if there is such a thing. Startled, Daniellé heard church bells from a cathedral ring.

The ring was enough to bring her back into reality. She began the slow walk down the railing to her car. She laughed at the thought of being saved by the bell, but in her laugh she slipped.

Daniellé looked down at the waters as she now was crawling back to her car. She reached the car feeling ashamed and relieved at the same time. The keys hung from the ignition, but she did not turn it on. In her soaked clothing, the car faced the orange traffic cones.

The rain poured off and on, with her phone buzzing from messages from Daryl, Angelia and her parents. It was selfish for her not to answer them. She was a coward for not responding, but she did not want the company right now.

She wanted permanent silence. She wanted to die.

Still lost in thought, Daniellé's phone rang a fourth with Daryl's number.

"Hello?" Daniellé answered quietly.

"Where are you? If I get another call from your mother!" Daryl's voice was full of concern and annoyance.

"Ray street." She replied.

"Well, what's the plan?" Daryl asked perturbed at her short answer.

"There is none." Daniellé replied.

"Are you coming back here?" Daryl asked.

"No. Tonight, I just need to be alone. Can you tell my mother?" Danielled asked.

"You ask a lot, lady. But fine. You should talk to her." Daryl suggested.

"Tomorrow." Daniellé answered.

"Be safe. I will leave the door unlocked in case you change your mind." Daryl commented as he hung up the phone.

He was one of those people whom always locked his door. Daniellé recalled him saying that trust doesn't belong on a one-way street.

The stars made their way out as nightfall approached. Stars were something missed by Daniellé in New York City. Sure, the neon lights and street lamps provided light, but the citizens of New York City were missing the beauty of nature. Perhaps, that is why they attempted it with bistro lights on rooftops.

Daniellé pushed down her seat lever to lay down against its gray cloth of the driver's seat. She was way too tall for this position, but tired enough to note care. All the nightmares she was having lately made sleep pointless. Every few hours she woke up screaming. At least if she woke up here, no one would hear her.

Come morning light filled the car from every angle. It was one way to assure that she would be up early. A new voicemail appeared on her phone. It was from the clinic saying they had results. She could stop by and retrieve them at any time.

I guess that means I can head that way. She thought.

This time the clinic's clerk told her it would only be a few minutes before Kelly talked with her. Daniellé looked around the room. It was filled with more children than adults. She leaned against the wall.

The secretary was right. No more than five minutes later nurse Kelly personally opened the door searching for Daniellé. The expression was a smile, but the dark circles under her eyes suggested she had not slept well.

"Come with me. How are you feeling?" Kelly spoke as she walked with Daniellé.

It was a wash, rinse and repeat of yesterday as Daniellé made her way up to the patient's table.

"Okay. I guess. You?" Daniellé answered.

"I am good. Busy day ahead. We ran your tests," Kelly started, "I am going to ask you some questions. They may be hard, but I want you to try to be brave for me. Okay?"

Daniellé nodded yes.

"Good. Do you remember what happened to you? Remember, it can stay confidential." Kelly assured.

"Not a lot, but some." Daniellé answered.

Daniellé's mouth gaped open in attempting to speak. The words did not want to surface, and her mouth hung open. She looked ashamed. It was true that she could not remember much, but there were a few things she knew.

"Did you check for STDS?" Daniellé asked desperately.

"Yes. I did. Everything on the panel was clean. You do not have to worry about that." Kelly smiled as she said the words.

Daniellé's heart lifted a little.

Thank God. She thought.

"Did someone force this on you?" Kelly asked calmly.

Daniellé was silent.

"Do you remember who?" Kelly was gathering information.

Daniellé remained silent.

"Not now please." Daniellé pleaded."Can I go?"

As she looked down at the papers she saw information about fertility and trauma groups along with a local women's shelter phone number. Nurse Kelly just nodded and escorted her to the front lobby.

"Take care." Kelly said as Daniellé walked out.

The drive to her father's house was only about an hour, but it took Daniellé nearly three. The first hour she stood still in her car at the clinic's papers reviewing everything. The next couple hours she felt the need to stop every so often due to pain or the feeling of a panic attack. The main issue was each time she began thinking more memories would surface causing what felt like a mental collapse.

Daniellé just wanted to move on with her life. Forget.

When she finally reached her father's street, she put the car in park. She knew that if she walked up the top of the subdivision she could see who was parked at the house. Three cars representing her mother, father and younger brother were in the driveway. It was time to face them.

She stood in front of the red painted door from her childhood. It opened before her hand reached the knob. Her beautiful blonde mother stood in front of her with long hair touching her hips.

"Oh, babygirl. I told you so." Escaped as the first words from her mother's lips as her arms wrapped around Daniellé, "At least you are home now."

Daniellé knew in that moment she would not be able to share what happened to her with her family or friends. They would not understand. They would not be able to handle the truth. She was barely handling it.

It would be her personal affliction. An affliction developed from her high fashion dream.

It was her fashion affliction.

Daniellé looked back up at her mother with her newly-fashioned mask on her face.

She said exactly what her mother needed to hear, "Yes. I'm home."

Dark as Ashes

Months Later.

I n the pitch darkness, Daniellé laid on a queen size mattress in the downstairs of her father's home. She felt like she had been laying there for centuries. She would not be surprised if there was a fossil imprint pressed into the bed's foam under her. Its carbon dating could reveal to the world what she already felt, long dead.

Daniellé's mind wondered as she analyzed her body. *Am I dead? No. Breathing? Yes. My leg? No. My arm? No.*

Her body was still paralyzed from her nightmare. Nightmares for Daniellé were a common occurence lately. Her brain would feel awake, but the rest of her body, especially her limbs would be numb. It was like her arms and legs didn't get the *wake up* memo. Her mouth felt sewn shut. Her eyes were open, and her eyelids felt taped to her eyebrows. The inability to blink was led to an uncomfortable dryness. Her right arm hung in freefall over the mattress's edge.

The last few weeks Daniellé had researched heavily the scientific phenomenon afflicting her. It was called sleep paralysis. Two words named this terrifying sense of losing one's self. The condition caused debate between being a sleep disorder and conscious anxiety. It was as if the brain stayed awake while the body remained in the crossfire of a dream and reality. Thus, losing control for even small movements.

Very few things leave someone more powerless than losing the ability to move their own body. Unable to shift a toe or turn the neck. Even shutting eyes is out of the person's control.

She was somewhat comforted in knowing her nightmares were not something she experienced alone, but at the same time, she did not enjoy belonging to the group called P.T.S.D.

In one study they even called people suffering, clinical particular cases. Science can provide beautiful elaborate reasons behind difficult problems, but in Daniellé's case it hardly ever answered how to directly fix the issue.

For Daniellé it happened about once a week. The other nights were already booked for night terrors and dreamless darkness, but once a week sleep paralysis would pencil itself into the calendar.

Perhaps, if she knew where this calendar resided she could better prepare herself for the transpiring events. But instead, she remained powerless.

She knew every inch of this basement. She knew the cream tile floor with the dark-mocha grout. She knew the five long walls were a shade of ivory her mother picked out during her childhood. It was long since her parents divorced, a decade ago, but she even remembered painting the walls. She knew this place, but perhaps it knew her better.

This basement knew all the places for darkness to induce Daniellé's fear. The basement knew when to produce unexplainable creaks and squeaks. The place she called home, knew how to create a terror-stricken Daniellé grew up baptist, methodist and at times, agnostic. With the mixture of religion, Daniellé had concluded she could not stand any of it.

When she was younger, Daniellé was drawn to the romanticized idea of church fellowship. The idea of belonging and acceptance from a group of fellow Jesus believers gave her joy.

Yet, she would see the same Jane Doe and John Smith on Sunday shaking hands at church to not even make eye contact with her family on Monday morning bus pickup.

Her mother would inform her church was about spending time with God and learning the proper way to live, but Daniellé could not see how God could be in places like this.

Despite the uncertainty of church, Daniellé still believed in God.

It was an inner core knowing of His existence. The same inkling of assurance kindled the dwindling fire in her to keep fighting for a future. So, when the paralysis nightmare began, and she laid in still, powerless.

All Daniellé could do was recite the Lord's prayer.

Daniellé was angry at the world in its entirety - especially humans. At one point in time she believed humans were innately good. Thus meaning, if given the choice between doing what is good and right, they would do good. Right? Perhaps not.

She was angry because people think they are powerful. They build their fantasy lives with fancy houses and careers. They surround themselves with money or fake relationships.

People will lie, cheat and steal for their wants, not just their needs.

Women will steal another's husband while cooking for their own.

Men will lie to his best friend to save himself.

A father will undercut his own son to get ahead financially- or vice versa.

They think they are untouchable, safe and happy, but during sleep paralysis moments no one can hear a soundless scream.

No earthly item or service can provide aid. These moments are for surrendering. All security once known is nonexistent.

No one and nothing can help. The only option is to pray. Daniellé did not survive New York City to die by fear's hand, but her night terror was taking it toll.

****

The cold basement air created a shivering sensation throughout Daniellé's body. Discomfort and anxiety consumed her in the darkness. She felt like someone was with her in the dark.

It not like light presence that comes along with an answered prayer.

This presence felt like walking in a dark parking lot with keys between knuckles. She felt like she needed to protect herself from it.

Logically speaking, Daniellé was overreacting.

Of course, she was alone in the room. Right?

It did not make sense that she could be alone, and then someone magically appear. But if this was true, then who was the tall shadowy man staring at her from the bottom bed frame?

The man was over six and a half feet tall. He was dark as twilight and succulent. In some cruel way he captivated her attention.

Daniellé found herself in an eye lock with her unwanted visitor. His elongated arms grazed over her feet. Daniellé begged for the ability to cry out or move, but she remained motionless.

Striped of her willpower her eyes stayed locked on his beaming red empty eye sockets. Long legs pressed into the mattress. Now, over her legs, Daniellé begged for salvation. His ghostly fingers reached her inner thighs pushing them apart. His body moved higher until his head faced her breasts.

Gravity locked Daniellé in place.

She knew what was going to happen next. She braced herself as this stranger like the ones before would have their way with her. Like countless times before, she provided no permission, but it did not matter.

They held power, and Daniellé held nothing.

The shadow man did not stop, but instead wrapped his elongated fingers around her neck. The size of his hands could lap around her neck twice.

As he continued, Daniellé's eyes bulged as her trachea felt like it could collapse.

Please just kill me. She pleaded.

It was almost dawn, but the room was still filled with darkness. Daniellé jolted from her slumber. A piercing scream escaped her lungs, and she knew then not only was she still alive, but she was not free from any of this madness. Her sheets were drenched from her sweat, and her limbs felt like they had finished a marathon.

She waited to hear any shuffling from upstairs. Her father was a heavy sleeper at the other end of the home. Daniellé knew he either could not hear her waking from her nightmares or he was too afraid to ask about them. Nonetheless, she was okay with not explaining her nightly screaming.

No noise came from upstairs, and Daniellé wrapped a satin robe around her body from the bedpost. The tile was cold beneath her feet as she walked to wash off the sweat from her face. The lights of the downstairs restroom did not match with remaining rooms. This bathroom was harshly lit. It was the type of light one would see in a television scene of an interrogation room.

When she looked in the mirror she felt like a fraud. Her hair was a faded pink from her previous phoenix red. She was no longer the flaming phoenix red head model.

She was nothing. So, if this was her interrogation, she was cracked at this confession.

Daniellé wanted to remove all evidence of being a former model. She wanted to be invisible to the world- the opposite of a top model in New York City.

An impulsive thought entered her mind. Two Halloweens ago she had dressed up as a cat. Not just a typical house cat, but a majestic cat like from the screenplay. She had gone to the store to buy temporary black hair coloring, but accidently purchased permanent. She caught the mistake before disaster struck.

She sorted through the cabinet toiletries until she found a beautiful woman with raven hair on a coloring box.

"Perfect." She announced to herself.

Daniellé followed the instructions and stepped into the shower with great relief. As excessive black coloring ran down the drain, Daniellé realized the irony of the situation.

"The phoenix is now as dark as ashes." Daniellé said as she accepted her new identity.

Writing for Salvation

There was no door to the kitchen, instead it was a direct connection from the stairs. This meant Daniellé clearly could tell her father ignored her new hair style as she walked up to the kitchen.

He had not spoken more than a few words at a time to her in over a month. Still upset over her deciding to spend her first night back home at Daryl's place, he was cold toward her.

It was not his fault though.

She knew her father could forgive her mishap of believing she preferred staying the night with Daryl instead of going straight home.

More importantly, she knew the truth would be something he would never let go. He would blame himself for letting Daniellé leave for New York City. No part of her wanted to give her father pain like hers.

He did not look up at her. Instead, he fiddled with a waffle maker making breakfast. The silence of the open room felt like boiling tension as she reached into the refrigerator for a bottled water.

She was doing well at hiding the physical evidence from her family with long sleeved tee shirts and pants. The weather was cold outside, so no one seemed to notice her choice of wardrobe attire as strange.

Daniellé returned down stairs feeling rejected. The television from upstairs echoed Star Wars intro music. Daniellé sat on the edge of her mattress wondering what to do with her day. She thought about pulling out a fresh canvas and paints from her packed things prior to her move to New York. She had no clue what she would paint thought as nothing seemed inspirational.

Digging through boxes looking for acrylic paints all she managed to find was pens and paper. She had not journaled since returning from New York City. She didn't want to relive her experiences by writing them down, but the bottling them all up idea was not working out either. Her experiences would show up in her nightmares, but perhaps if she wrote them down then she could get a decent night's sleep.

Her writing started out sounding more like a prayer than a journal entry. A few paragraphs in, Daniellé was writing from the memory about her breakdown on the New York rooftop.

She wrote about how she would never heal from what God let happen to her. She wrote of how it felt like to be lied to by Him. He said she was His child. If God loved her why would he let torture and rape happen?

She could not write those words down though. So, instead she transcribed the events of the rooftop. She unraveled all the chaos in her head on paper, and when finished seven pages of torture.

The papers stared at her.

A therapeutic breath released from her lungs. It was like the words on the page were no longer inside of her. It was disassociating bliss. Writing could be Daniellé's salvation from this anguish living inside of her and threatening her very existence.

An insane thought entered Daniellé's mind as she folded the paper into an envelope style.

I could give this to Dad. She thought.

Without thinking this completely through, Daniellé hurried up the stairs again to see her father sitting on the couch watching *Star Wars* with his waffles. His head did not turn when he saw his daughter hovering beside him. She pushed for his attention anyways.

"I am thinking of writing a book about New York." Daniellé said nervously.

He did not give a sign that he was listening, but he must have heard her.

"Will you please read these pages when you get a moment? Maybe tell me your thoughts?" She asked.

"Sure." He replied.

It was the first word she had heard from him today, and it was enough to give her hope. She placed the seven pages on the coffee table next to his plate and walked away to give him privacy. She did not want to actually see his facial expression as he read her soul on paper.

As she walked away her mind went haywire. *If he knows, he could help me. Would he be appalled? Would he think it was my fault? Isn't it?*

Gabriel messaged Daniellé asking if she would like to get lunch at 2:00 p.m. She had not seen him since she returned, but she accepted the invite to a BBQ restaurant in town.

Up until this point she was being a hermit crab. Most of her friends did not know of her return and she was avoiding the few who did know. Most of her friends thought she was ghosting them.

She still had not shared much with Gabriel either. He practically saved her life, but she did not know if he could help her any further. Sure the modeling agency was a complete scam. He had proved it to her. But the whole crime was so organized. She had no idea how to fight high-end criminals.

Even if she knew where to start, the threats were terrifying. The danger was real, and they could kill her for it.

At least now she was alive and away from them. She was free, but was being free enough?

Gabriel's eyes lit up with questions as they sat down with BBQ meals. Daniellé was not hungry, so she had simply copied Gabriel's meal choice. He insisted it be his treat, and he was starting to eat most of her food too.

"Nice hair. Janelle once colored her hair black. She looked like a whole new person." Gabriel commented.

Janelle was Gabriel's beautiful and brilliant wife. The two of them were the happiest couple Daniellé knew. It was as if their honeymoon stage never ended, even after eight years of marriage.

"Thank you. The red needed to go." Daniellé smirked feeling better about her new look.

The conversation faded to silence as Gabriel continued eating. Daniellé wondered what all she had missed since she last saw him. Gabriel was planning to run for political office again, and she wondered why he cared so much for politics. Nonetheless, she liked the idea of someone like him in office. Gabriel was not the type of person to be swayed by money. He based his decisions off morality and family values.

Gabriel explained what needed to be done differently in local government for much of lunch. It was not until he was done with his food and Daniellé had nibbled some, that he changed the topic to her life.

"Are you planning to go back to school?" He asked.

"I will. I just do not know what to do when I graduate anymore." Daniellé shrugged.

"Well, you will have the entire school year to figure that part out. You might as well finish." Gabriel commented.

"I guess." Daniellé said, at a loss for words.

"Let's get some to-go refills before we leave." Gabriel suggested as he stood.

Daniellé grabbed their cups.

Daniellé returned home feeling a little better about her future. She thought finishing school would change things for the better. It could shut the door on the past. When she walked back in the house, her father had not moved from the couch. It was not that he was lazy, but most likely exhausted from a seventy-hour work week.

Daniellé saw the papers shuffled on the coffee

table. *So, he did read them.* She thought.

Her dad lifted his head as he yawned. Daniellé became very nervous as she gathered her courage to ask his opinion of her work.

"Did you read it?" Daniellé asked choking on her words.

"Yeah. I read it. Did not make much sense though?" Her assessed.

"Oh, really? Because I thought it could be the start to a book about..I mean I could start again. What's wrong with it?" Daniellé searched for explanation.

"Well, I guess I am just not your target audience." He commented.

"Oh, okay." She concluded the conversation.

Daniellé walked away not knowing if her father was short with her from still being angry or simply had no interest in her writing.

Maybe, this could just be for her. It could be the closest thing she could have for therapy.

It did not make sense? At the time it did not even make sense to me? Daniellé thought.

She laid on the bed again feeling defeated. She could not talk to her father. She could not talk to Gabriel. She could not talk to anyone. Once again she was reminded her pain was her own cross to bear.

She fell asleep crying until she was awoken by the front door slamming open.

"Hey, you have lunch,yet?" Daniellé's brother asked their father upstairs.

Gideon was a few years younger than Daniellé. He was the strong and silent type, which made it difficult for the siblings to be close. Gideon looked a lot like her, but he had one blue eye and one green eye. Whereas, Daniellé's were purely green. They both would be dirty blonde if Daniellé had not colored her hair. The closest sibling connection was their strong resemblance.

"Yeah, I ate earlier. There is food in the fridge though. Your sister is downstairs by the way." Father commented.

Daniellé imagined Gidoen's eyes widening at their father's words. Gideon had last spoke to Daniellé during a fight when she first returned. He had commented how badly she looked, and she had screamed at him. Since then, he had consumed his schedule with work and friends. He no longer lived in the house, so it was easy to avoid her.

She wanted to see him though, so she slowly made her way upstairs.

When their eyes met, there was no excitement. They remained in neural tones as Gideon greeted her with a nod. The Winter family could hold a grudge like no other family.

"Nice hair." Gideon commented.

"It was time for a change," Daniellé replied.

She joined her father and brother in front of the television. Together they all watched the next *Star Wars* in mostly silence as Gideon cooked. Daniellé watched how heroes won and villains fell, and wished life could be as simple as it was on screen.

How to Save a Life

After her talk with Gabriel, Daniellé enrolled back into college. Courses had already started, but she had a strong standing from previous years and good connections with her professors. She promised them she would catch up and be a perfect student.

She had decided isolation from the world was just an additive to her torture. This was her attempt to be normal again. She was going to earn her college degree - even if she did not know what to do with it.

With this expensive tuition she thought she could at least utilize the college student services for mental health.

Daniellé was scared to share the threatening messages she had been receiving or the endless night terrors with her friends or family. Instead, she thought a medical professional sworn to confidentiality could help.

As she sat in a brightly colored counseling room across from a woman who did not seem much older than herself, Daniellé questioned her decision.

This was her second visit to see Dr. Kertz of the three free student therapy sessions. The first one was filled with introductions and family background, and left

Daniellé feeling more hopeless than satisfied. It was not enough for her to give up though, as the chirpy woman stared at her eager to help.

"I'm glad you decided to come today. How are you feeling? You seemed upset when you left last time." Dr. Kertz asked.

"I was upset, but I know this takes time." Daniellé shrugged.

The process of visiting a shrink was odd to Daniellé. It reminded her of the times she watched *Pretty Little Liars* or *Revenge*. The therapists in the shows always talked in riddles and had secret agendas. Daniellé did not think Dr. Kertz had a secret agenda, but she definitely talked in riddles.

It might have been for the limited time or sessions, but Dr. Kertz did not ask for stories of what happened to Daniellé to where she felt like she needed therapy. Instead, Dr. Kertz asked questions in an interview style.

For Daniellé, it felt like crash dieting memory detox. Daniellé was supposed to answer the questions in order to release the bad memories from within her. The idea would be only good memories would remain on the inside and the bad memories were released from her.

Crash diets never worked for Daniellé and this was not working either.

Reviewing the events with Dr. Kertz was increasing the night terrors, paranoia and panic attacks. As a result, Daniellé stopped sleeping at night and studied instead. She would only put down the books when daylight arised.

Perhaps Daniellé's expectations were too high. There was no way Dr.Kertz was going to be able to fix her in three sessions. So far, things were becoming far worse, and only one session remained.

She had no idea how to save her life from falling apart, but she was pretty sure Dr. Kertz did not either.

During their second sessions, they managed to uncover one reality together. With Dr. Kertz questions Daniellé now understood what could have prevented everything that happened to her.

****

Five months before returning home.

I am too busy right now. I'm at modeling agency conference.

These were the summarized words explained to Daniellé from her agent.

The desperate Daniellé seeked help from her mother agent, Felicia. Daniellé knew the modeling conference Felicia was referencing. It was located in New York City, not too far from where Kathleen and Daniellé's hotel.

The purpose of the event was for modeling agencies to scout talent from smaller agencies. It was a long shot to be scouted at the conference, but somehow models were convinced they would be discovered there. Models would pay a few thousand dollars and most of the time only come home feeling defeated or with a modeling award. Rarely, did they actually be signed or discovered.

Daniellé had thought the conference was just used to get the hopes up for aspiring models and profit agencies.

The point here was Felicia could have taken Daniellé's call.

This rejection and negligence of care took place right before Daniellé's reckoning.

It was another memory Daniellé was forced to keep because it reminded her of how differently her life could have gone. If Felicia had just cared enough to take her calls or meet her. If she would have listened or held any responsibility for her talent, then her life would have a much different story now.

"She is not going to help." Daniellé delicately said to Kathleen.

Both souls were crushed.

It could have been different if the agent had done proper due diligence. If she had done so, it would have prevented the countless assaults.

****

When Daniellé's therapy session concluded, she decided to confront the agent. Daniellé was not sure if Felicia had any moral compass, but she needed to realize what she had done.

Daniellé was scared and infuriated as she told Justine face-to-face what happened in New York. She did not explain each detail of the rapes but she confronted her with the aftermath. She showed Felicia her scars and explained to Felicia exactly to who she sent her talent.

Instead Felicia treated her as worthless as the men who had taken advantage of her. Daniellé was just one of thousands of talent on her roster. It seemed Felicia thought Daniellé was less than human, instead she could not profit from a scarred up model and just wanted Daniellé to go away.

She suggested Daniellé be released from her modeling contract immediately. She had no sympathy. She claimed no responsibility. From that moment forward, Daniellé understood the deep problems rooted in the modeling industry. She had seen first hand the abuses of an unregulated field.

There was no human resources department or modeling union to report these transgressions.

She was powerless.

Daniellé knew what had happened to her was going to keep happening to thousands of other models across the nation and globe. She wondered how many times it had happened before her, and in these moments, she had never been some consumed by rage in her life.

Section Three: Exposure

Won't you see me, or is this just a mirror within me, Put these tears back inside my eyes, no lenses.

No, I don't know what I need, but it is not more time, therapy or a degree .

None of those will save me from this strobe light condition of a monster inside of me.

My picture-perfect image is my best lie of makeup and pretty little lies.

I am tearing at my own skin to make it match inside and I am dying my hair so no one sees it turning white.

Expose all these wounds from infection and the lies of deception.

Dark Web Places

Spiders can be the most extraordinary creatures. They know their surroundings, limitations and prey. From protein silk they weave elaborate patterned webs hidden from their unsuspecting victims.

Before the prey can understand the darkness capturing them, it is too late. Injected with the malicious venom of the predator their life is over.

The spider takes what they wish and casts out the lifeless prey.

****

When the first email entered Daniellé's inbox, she deleted it thinking it was spam. When the second message entered her inbox, she was more curious.

While waiting for her school lecture, she decided to open it.

This email ignited terror within her.

She had been casually chatting with a schoolmate, but now she slammed her computer shut and she packed her school bag.

"Please, tell Professor Naugh, I had an emergency." Daniellé asked her friend.

Daniellé rushed through the students entering the lecture hall as she darted out. She felt another panic attack arising.

No. No. No. This can't be happening. Daniellé worried as she now pulled the email up on her phone.

Daniellé found an empty hallway. She sat on the cold tile floor. Swinging her backpack to her side she did not want to believe what she saw. She wanted to believe she was hallucinating or her phone was playing an evil trick on her.

The email's sender was unknown. All of her computer knowledge amounted to nothing.

The message did not say much, yet like a spider capturing it prey, Daniellé could not escape this attack.

Your parents shall know. Your friends shall know. Your teachers saw see. Just how much of a whore you really are. The sender wrote.

If it had been words, Daniellé could have been fine. She would have brushed it off as an empty threat.

It was not just words though.

She looked at the email attachments and knew now what a fallen phoenix really looked like when it burst into flames.

Now, Daniellé knew the torment she lived was not made up or erasable.

Photos of her undressed and battered were on her screen.

More emails filled her inbox with threats and horror. With each arrival Daniellé felt raped and violated again and again.

She felt pain throughout her body as if it was happening all over again. Her neck felt like a metal bar struck it. Her legs throbbed, and a migraine commenced.

She understood this was not happening again, but somehow, she was reliving everything at once.

Daniellé dialed Gabriel's number.

He did not answer.

She looked at the images one-by-one. She reached for her arm where she had once stitched herself up. Her fingertips grazed over the area. Her frail fingers moved downward to where her ribs once ached so badly that she thought she would die from the pain.

Wanting to forget, Daniellé covered her

eyes. "It will never end." She cried.

Daniellé was desperate as she stood to walk toward the exit. Outside, she had a choice to make. To her left a mile away would be her car. She could hide there or driveway until no one could find her. She could become the lifeless prey of the dark web spider.

But Daniellé walked right because she knew less than a mile this way was a police station.

She did not stop to look at her phone, but instead her footsteps were automatic. When she arrived, a woman walked out a wooden door, much like the one from the New York police station. The lady was tall and looked strong enough to win a fight with any man or woman. Yet, her face looked kind enough to cradle a newborn.

"Can I help you?" The woman was assertive as she

spoke. "I hope so." Daniellé answered nervously.

Daniellé handed the woman her phone with the email still open.

"I'm Detective Ryan. You can call me Wendy," She greeted, "Come inside, let's talk."

Brotherly Love

Vital signs.

All the healthcare books Danielle read had chapters about body temperature, respiration and blood pressure.

Mental illness.

Daniellé hung on the words of her professors. She thought heavily about the term's depression, anxiety and PTSD.

Suicide.

One of the leading causes of death for young teens and adults.

Daniellé was becoming used to being a statistic. She was once a genetically favored model statistic. She was a rape statistic. She was a human trafficking statistic.

It was sinking in now, that she was going to become a suicide statistic.

Daniellé had not fight left it in her. She had tried reaching out. She did all three sessions with the therapist, but had no money to continue. She had gone to the police, and even though Detective Ryan wanted to help her, the evidence was untraceable.

She had tried to write to her father, but it did not make any sense. Daniellé no longer believed she was meant to live. She was a universal flaw, that needed correcting. She was not meant to live happily-ever after. She was not meant to live at all.

Daniellé stared at the medicine cabinet. She thought about writing a letter, but that did not go well the first time.

For the last few days, she thought of all the possibilities of how to end her life. She considered walking into traffic or a car wreck. She considered blades, a gun or going back to the bridge. The only thing stopping her from these options was not wanting to hurt anyone else in the process of ending her life.

She stared at the empty medicine bottle as she waited. All she needed to do now was wait for it to have an effect on her. She would fade out of this world into whatever was ahead of her.

She looked down at her wrists. Her skin was so think it looked like thin paper.

The textbook said it was a central nervous system depressant.

Daniellé never discovered the medical cocktail her violators had poisoned her with during her torment. It fulfilled their purpose though, and up until this moment Daniellé was terrified of things going into her body.

Even at the health clinic, she had to remind herself that they were trying to help her, not hurt her.

Daniellé felt nauseous thinking of the New York house. As her eyes shut, she saw the kaleidoscope of men's faces and bodies hovering over her. Each pulling, stroking, ripping, and forcing themselves on her.

Even death was not going to be peaceful for her. At least, it would all be over soon.

Daniellé gagged on her own vomit as Gideon threw her to her side. His eyes were filled with fury as he banged hard on her back.

Daniellé gasped for breath. This was not fair. She was being robbed of even this choice.

Crossed between pain and disbelief, Gideon stared at his sister.

"What the hell do you think you are doing?" Gideon yelled at her.

Daniellé blank faced remembered how far they had came from their childhood. Once upon a time, she had protected her little brother from the horrors of the world. She had protected him from their parents violent fights, school bullies and even failing grades.

He had never seen violence, rejection or pain. She had made sure of it.

Until now. Now, she was the source of it for him.

He kept screaming at her with broken eyes and heart.

Gideon collapsed into her lap crying, "I love you. Do you know that?"

He repeated it over and over. Daniellé could not remember a time he had ever said those words to her. He had never been so vulnerable.

He stayed on the floor with her, sitting in silence. Daniellé did not run away but laid her head upon his.

The blood flow returning to her was painful, and everything about this was beyond excruciating. During all her thoughts, she never considered how she would still manage to hurt someone dying in this way.

"Never again, okay? Never again." Gideon

pleaded. "Never again." Daniellé answered.

Erika

D anielle recalled being told the best books were about a hero's journey. These stories were about conquering the unbeatable.

But she disagreed.

For her, the best books were not about heroes. She did not believe in heroes. For her, the best stories were about people constantly battling to survive. She did not believe in heroes vs villains - just humans in constant battle within themselves to survive.

Daniellé had promised her brother to never attempt to take her life again. She realized killing herself would only transfer her pain to others.

So, she decided to live with the pain.

Gideon was not going to forgive her any time soon though. To give him space and herself a fresh start, she accepted an invite to move in with her friend Daniel and his two roommates Bethany and Ed. In order to afford rent, tuition and general living costs, Daniellé interviewed and accepted three part-time jobs. She was going to work at her college as a medical researcher in one department and a greenhouse manager in another.

On the weekends, she would spend both days as a server for an Italian restaurant. Along with a full course schedule, this was her master plan to stay busy.

At least this way she would be a productive member of society.

For the next three months this plan worked like a hamster wheel for her life. She enjoyed her roommates, even if they were all kind of party animals. They respected Daniellé's dedication to work and school, and did not bother her. It became an unspoken rule that while she had the chemistry book out or work uniform on, no one bugged her.

On a dark night while Daniellé studied for an important exam, a stranger would stumble into the house with Bethany. Daniellé was not expecting anyone to be home, so she was studying in the living room.

Daniel and Ed were at work, and Bethany had told her earlier that week she would be staying with a friend after a party.

Something must have gone wrong though, as now Bethany and a heavily intoxicated woman were interrupting her study time.

At first, Daniellé ignored them as she stared packing up her things to study elsewhere, but when she looked at the stranger, she almost felt like she knew her.

The woman's eyes were swollen and hazy. Her mascara was smudged from tears and she clearly was not sober. Her clothes were slightly tattered, and she reeked of cigarettes. Clearly, she had been out partying with Bethany.

Daniellé's trance was broken when Bethany sprinted across the room between her and the mysterious visitor.

"Hey, you are not going anywhere right? I have to run to the store." Bethany asked.

"Yeah, why?" Daniellé replied confused.

"Cool. Can you keep an eye on my friend? Have you seen Daniel or Ed?" She asked.

Bethany was on high alert for something. Daniellé just did not understand what.

"They are working." Daniellé answered.

"Good." Bethany replied as she slammed the door behind her.

Daniellé found herself in a new role as babysitter. She closed her book and went to sit next to the mystery woman laying on her couch. She scanned the lady up and down until a rush of understanding overcame her. The woman did not look up at her, but instead her face was planted into a pillow.

Daniellé saw the reflection of herself in the woman. Daniellé saw herself all those months ago.

She saw how the woman tucked her hands between her thighs as she laid in a cradling position. She felt the aura of loss and vulnerability surrounding her.

Daniellé felt light-headed as horrendous memories rushed back into the forefront of her mind. She stood to run away to the closest restroom. She was going to vomit, and her legs grew weak at each step.

The woman on the couch did not notice. Captivated in her own misery, she was not paying attention to Daniellé. Life as the woman had known it had changed -just like for Daniellé.

In the restroom, Daniellé closed the door behind her. How many times had she stared in the mirror as she begged herself to come up with answers.

What do I do? Daniellé fell to the floor.

She remembered when Daryl met her on the floor of their old home. Months later, he had a new roommate and she had pretended that night never happened. Now, it was confronting her in a whole new way. past. It had been almost forty minutes before Bethany returned to the house.

"Daniellé, where are you?" She yelled. "Restroom."

Daniellé yelled back.

"I need you." She commanded.

Daniellé wanted to reject her. She wanted to say she was busy. Yet, she opened the door to aid her friend.

"This is Erika." Bethany introduced the strangers, "I have to take care of a few things. But she isn't feeling well. I have to leave again, but in the bag is some medicine. Can you help? Consider it practice for becoming a doctor."

Daniellé respected how Bethany kept Erika's privacy. She agreed.

Bethany left behind a bag with Gatorade, maxi pads, pain killers, food and other first aid items.

"Are you awake?" Danielled kneeled beside Erika.

Erika said nothing.

Daniellé attempted dry humor, "You know my problem? I am studying for a medical exam, that I already know I am going to fail."

Erika faced away from her, silent.

After a few awkward minutes, Daniellé stood up to fetch her book. She returned to sit on the floor below Erika's face.

Another ten minutes past before Erika asked, "Can you hand me that?"

"This? You like Gatorade?" Daniellé responded. "Not really?" Erika commented.

"You want tea? Like Earl Grey, not that weird herbal stuff?" Daniellé stood up as she offered.

"I hate herbal tea." Erika said as she lifted her head.

"Then it's settled. I am making Earl Grey." Daniellé declared.

When Daniellé left the room, Erika sat up from lying down.

Daniellé returned with two fresh cups of tea.

"Well, you did better than me. I would have run away as soon as I left the room." Daniellé said as she handed the cup to Erika.

Daniellé did not need to ask Erika about what happened. She already knew by her barren eyes and the blood stain of her jeans.

She knew where the bruises between Erika's legs would be and the pain she would feel the following days.

And maybe, Erika knew that Daniellé knew. Over the next two hours, Erika explained everything that transpired that night to her. At times, Daniellé's breath would be taken away and at others she wanted to reach out and hold the woman. She wanted to tell her she would not judge her, and she was not alone. Danille almost shared her story with Erika, but in the end, she decided not to disclose.

"I know a detective we can call..." Daniellé suggested.

Uncharacteristic Noel

Weeks had passed since Daniellé and Erika's hospital trip. Semester exams had finished, and Daniellé had developed a nice routine.

Every morning, she would rise from her bed. She would leave her nightmares tucked in between her freshly made bed. Then she would go to work. She even started making new friends and spending time with her roommates.

Life was fine, and she was living contently with the physical and emotional pain. But now that exams were finished, Christmas was the topic of every discussion.

In the deep south, Christmas is not an optional holiday. Instead of being a single day, it consumes an entire winter season. Soon after pumpkin spice lattes leave Starbuck's menu, Christmas lights go up across town. Most of the time before even Halloween or Thanksgiving has passed.

In the Winter household, Christmas was a busy time of year.

After several years of divorce, Christmas was known to be split amongst parents. Christmas Eve and Christmas morning belonged to mother, and Christmas afternoon belonged to father. Christmas night, if Daniellé could make it through, belonged to friends. Most years she spent it with Angelina's family.

This Christmas felt like a gaping hole as Daniellé felt the continual rock in her chest weighing her down.

Over the last few days, an annoying ringing had developed in Daniellé's head. It sounded like someone had turned on a television frequency only she could hear, and it was beginning to make her feel batty. If people knew her story, they probably would understand if she was starting to go a little insane.

Daniellé had started running to alleviate her pain. She had heard about runners high, and at ten miles a day, it was like her personal health care plan. But no matter how far she ran, the ringing did not stop.

So, Daniellé tried writing. She wrote like writing was going out of style with books filled with enough information and night terrors to write several novels. This too, did not stop the ringing in her ears.

It was becoming unbearable for her.

On an uncharacteristic Christmas night, Daniellé felt like another mental breakdown was bound to happen. She had made it through Christmas morning and afternoon with a fake smile on her face. She showed gratitude for gifts and sang along to Christmas hymns, but secretly she was just waiting for it all to be over.

When it came time to head over to Angelina's house, Daniellé felt compelled to take a detour to Noel Lake. With her jeans pressed into the cold grass, Christmas sweater and curled raven hair, Daniellé looked out at the lake's waters. Tousling her hair, she missed her natural blonde locks.

What happened in New York was not the only chapter in Daniellé's life she wished she could forget. Looking back, the reasoning behind Daniellé's return to Noel Lake was because she had left this chapter open, too.

Daniellé was always running away from the pain in her life instead of facing it.

Daniellé was tired of running away.

She was ready to face all the demons of her past, and being at Noel Lake was one of them.

Daniellé's high school memory came to mind as she looked at a far off island in the middle of the lake.

****

"And this is my cousin, Ekekiel. His brother is not around, but his name is Tychicus." Viviana, a friend of Daniellé, introduced a tall, handsome boy holding the reins to a horse to Daniellé.

Viviana, of Viv for short, was a spunky, headstrong girl two years older than Daniellé. They had met at school, and had hit it off right away. Soon, they were going everywhere together. Today, they were at Viv's stables with Viv introducing her cousin.

Daniellé found everything about Ezekiel beautiful.

"Have you ever ridden a horse?" Ezekiel asked his new friend.

"Does a merry-go-round count?" Daniellé was hiding her attractive behind humor.

Viv was smart and picked up on the social cues right away. She made an excuse to go to find food for the horses.

"Take life by the reins." Ezekiel said pointing to the horse.

As the months passed by, Ezekiel would continually be showing Daniellé how to take life by the reins, but most importantly showed her who controlled those reins.

Once during a walk, Ezekiel explained who he loved most on this Earth. She was intrigued.

"I will not let you go until you bless me. Do you know who said that?" Ezekiel pop-quizzed Daniellé.

Talking about Christ meant the two of them were outcasts at school, but they were both fine with it. She believed in God, and even though she did not have all the pieces of the puzzle right, she trusted God's plan.

Ezekiel's love was patient, and he encouraged Daniellé's thirst for adventure. When she left for her modeling gigs he would remind he was praying for her safety.

The two of them were perfection, until the day at Noel Lake.

It was a September day like any other September day. Pumpkin spice lattes were on the Starbuck's menu and autumn leaves had started falling.

Two competitive swimmer brothers challenged one another to a contest. Like most days, Ezekiel did not let asthma stop him from beating his little brother in a race.

But this September day took Ezekiel away with an asthma attack in the waters of Noel Lake.

On that day, Daniellé would have the first unfixable crack in her heart. For the first time, she would question God's existence and his decision to take Ezekiel away.

Daniellé did not cry at his funeral the way others did around her. She had written a long letter of their time together, and his parents allowed her to tuck it within his casket.

She had not gone to Noel Lake since. In a way, she blamed the waters for taking away her love.

****

Daniellé's memory stopped when her boots slid in the shore's mud. For a moment she thought about throwing off her boots and making the journey to the island herself. But even now, Ezekiel was keeping her grounded.

The ringing in her ears grew louder as her eyes filled with tears.

"Please, please stop!" Daniellé begged.

She coughed as the cold air burned her lungs.

"What do you want from me!" Daniellé yelled at God, "You took Ezekiel. You took my dreams. You gave them my body. Over and over you let them have me. What do you want from me! Why am I still alive! You let me parents devour one another, year after year. You let Ezekiel die, but you won't let me die? You let Adam beat me. You let the letters and threats torment me. You abandoned me. I loved you, and you left me here to rot. Why!"

Daniellé scratched at the earth and threw a tantrum like a small child.

She wasn't finished yet though as she kept yelling, "You let Gideon find me. You let Daryl and church bells save me. You watched me dream. I worked so hard. Why God? Please, just tell me. I don't want to live anymore. I demand to know why!"

Her voice lowered to a whisper and the ringing grew louder. Her hands cupped her ears.

The waves crashed against the shore, and in this moment Daniellé was ready, eager to see her creator face-to-face for her answers.

Her wrath was calmed in mere moments as she heard it.

Not yet. You do not get to be done yet. Tell it and do something about it. The voice commanded.

This made no sense to her. She knew she had heard it, but she was alone. Yet, the words repeated in her head wanting acceptance.

Erika was why, the girls of the New York house were why, all of the human trafficking and sexual assualt victims without a voice were why.

She was why.

God had planted a seed in Daniellé.

Most seeds are nurtured by a gardener, but she grew among the weeds and thorns.

God had allowed the weeds, harsh sun and parasites to come into her life, but just as He commanded this Lake Noel shore to only go so far, he only let them hurt her so far.

God had known the backstory. He had known her purpose.

Daniellé surrendered. She knew what she was going to need to do now. She was no longer a model. She was not just a statistic, but she was something the world had not yet seen.

Daniellé needed to become the model who stopped traffic.

Acknowledgments

Since the release of *Models Stop Traffic: How to Dodge Enslavement in Pursuit of Your Dream to Become the Next Top Model*, I have been given the privilege to progress and serve in the advancement of human rights and freedom for human trafficking survivors and other victims of exploitation.

During this time, a vast support network of all ages, demographics, careers and nationalities have joined or partnered with me in our shared efforts. To everyone involved, these partnerships have become heavily meaningful in my life.

I would like to thank a few key individuals in helping with the creation of this book, service to combat exploitation and the assistance of my personal healing journey. Among these individuals are Wendy Elliot, Dr. Jessica Vera and the Parma-Vera household, Ricardo Rios, Sara Zitt, Chloe Bellande, Holly Cusick, The Survivor Blog Community, and my family.

Lastly, I would like to give my ongoing appreciation to everyone who has donated to support. You all are the fuel that is driving our awareness.

Thank you.

Author: Airica D. Kraehmer

Airica D. Kraehmer, nicknamed **Air**, is a survivor-activist, CEO of Storytelling Marketing, Founder of The Survivor Blog: Flying with Air and author of the novels *Models Stop Traffic, Trafficking Aftermath, and INVINCIBLE.*

As a survivor-activist, Air has spent the last several years combating trafficking with public speaking awareness in the United States and France!

Her latest accomplishment is working with the French government, Prime Minister of Gender Equality Marlene Schiappa, The Model Alliance, and international brands:

Loreal, Chanel, Kering, ELLE, LVMH to establish modeling industry regulations.

Air has worked extensively in her efforts to educate others about what human trafficking looks like - in all its ugly forms. As part of these efforts, Air contributes daily to The Survivor Blog, where she and other survivors confront all challenges and successes toward ending human trafficking.

She truly believes that we are the models who will stop trafficking in the United States and across the globe.

Contact Information:
Website: www.airicakraehmer.com
Email: contact@airicakraehmer.com

Social Media:
Facebook: www.facebook.com/airicakraehmer
Instagram: www.instagram.com/airicakraehmer